MW00669236

The
FULFILL
YOUR SOUL'S
PURPOSE
WORKBOOK

The
FULFILL
YOUR SOUL'S
PURPOSE

WORKBOOK

A GUIDE FOR SELF-STUDY

How to Find Your Life Mission
and Live with Intention

Naomi Irene Stephan, Ph.D
Sue Carroll Moore, LCSW

Acknowledgements

The authors wish to thank the following people who have given us invaluable help and support in the creation of this workbook:Julie Burns, Susan Flint, Ginny Mahoney, Dr. Sophie Mills, Deborah Pace, and Jean Williams. Special thanks to Stillpoint Publishing for use of their cover art, design by Karen Savary.

We also gratefully acknowledge our clients, whose dedication to their journey gave us the inspiration to write this book, and whose suggestions and feedback kept us on track.

Life Mission Associates
14 Cedarwood Drive
Asheville, N. C. 28803
1• 800 • 957-8888 (message line)

Copyright © 1997 by Sue Carroll Moore and Naomi Irene Stephan

All rights reserved. No part of this book may be reproduced without written permission from the publisher, except by a reviewer. No part of this book may be stored in a retrieval system, or transmitted in any form or by any other means electronic, mechanical, photocopying (except where noted in the text), recording, or other, without written permission from the publisher.

This book is manufactured in the United States of America.

The Fulfill Your Soul's Purpose Workbook: A Guide to Self-Study
Formerly: The Finding Your Life Mission™ Workbook: A Guide to Self-Study

ISBN: 0-9631262-8-8

1. Self-actualization (Career/Life Management)—Problems, exercises, etc.
2. Creative assessment—Problems, exercises, etc.

Poetry Class

write anything
on a piece of paper

a phone number
a conundrum
a recipe
your name
a want ad for used firewood
the letter
        Z

write anything
blankness blossoms into meaning
words float forth
from silence

distinct specificity

        with felicity.

Sue Carroll Moore

Contents

Introduction

This edition of *The Fulfill Your Soul's Purpose Workbook* is a companion guide to Dr. Naomi Stephan's book, *Fulfill Your Soul's Purpose—Ten Creative Paths to Your Life Mission,* published by Stillpoint International in 1994. We offer this updated workbook at the enthusiastic suggestion of readers and clients who attained new clarity of purpose and sense of direction by completing the structured program of exercises contained in an earlier edition titled, *The Finding Your Life Mission™ Workbook.* The workbook may be used for individual self-study, as a study guide for FYLM workshops, or as the curriculum for a Life Mission support group.

While offering new exercises and material, this edition of the workbook has at its core the same philosophy as its predecessor: each individual has a unique purpose in life that only she or he can fulfill. For some, this purpose was manifested at an early age others awake to their missions later in life.

The need for such a structured guide is greater than ever. With so many corporations "downsizing" and "dejobbing," more and more people are facing uncertain futures. Many who have looked outside of themselves for definition and purpose in life now find themselves adrift.

There are many valuable books to help the unemployed regain footholds in a changing job market through structured skills assessment, market analysis, or résumé writing. Our self-help program, however, emphasizes core values, individual responsibility, and personal assessment. As the American dream of unlimited economic expansion fades from sight, we urge you to turn inward for meaning, fulfillment and satisfaction. Dig deep. What are you here to achieve? Why have you come into this particular life? What special niche are you destined to fill? Through honest self-study you can enjoy a thrilling, zestful connection with your soul's purpose, which will empower you to make vital career and life decisions.

This process is not necessarily easy, nor can it be completed in one simple step. A friend of Pablo Casals noticed that the famous cellist spent a great deal of time every morning tuning his cello to get the "E" to sound just right. Why, the friend wondered, did Casals take such pains doing something so routine? Didn't he know how to tune his cello after all these years? "Finding the E is something you have to do every day," Casals explained.

Finding your mission is like finding the "E." It is an exciting but exacting task that connects you to your highest good. Your mission is there—and has been there—all the time. But it requires a commitment from you to discover and manifest it. This workbook offers creative tools and techniques to help you find your own perfect pitch. There is no time like the present to begin so that you, too, can make beautiful music and fulfill your Life Mission—your soul's purpose for this lifetime.

If you are not living your mission now, you cannot afford to wait any longer. Start working the exercises. Begin your quest for self discovery and enlightenment. Use this workbook to motivate, guide and steer you toward the mission you are meant to express. We the authors stand by you on your journey every step of the way.

The principles outlined here build on *Fulfill Your Soul's Purpose* (FYSP). This workbook is not intended to replace FYSP, but is a companion to its theory, discussions and case histories. We will refer you to specific sections or modules in FYSP which we encourage you to read in conjunction with your work here. Our basic mission principles emphasize the following:

1) Life Mission Concept

Life is a personal mission bestowed on each one of us. It is not a deep secret accessible only to some blessed initiates. Your mission is a cohesive, clear and specific guide for one individual—you. It describes the gift you have to share with the world, the way you intend to carry it out and for whom it is intended. It is your special endowment.

2) Nature of Mission: The String of Pearls

A mission is the sum total of everything you hold dear. We liken it to a string of pearls, encompassing and reflecting a number of talents, gifts, interests, passions and abilities—each one a pearl—which, when strung together, forms your mission. Viewed as all the things you love, a mission empowers you to access many facets of yourself within one common reference point.

3) Use of Mission

A mission is the channeled use of your most creative energy. Your being and action must reflect your mission, or you squander your energy and deprive the world of your gifts. Like any gift, a mission is only useful when it is received, unwrapped, and given back to the world.

4) Mission and Purpose

We define soul's purpose as the central theme of your soul, and mission as its particular application in this lifetime. Your mission is thus a beacon and blueprint, a unifying principle. You can express it in many ways, through careers, avocations, hobbies, or interests. Certain phases of your life might require differing applications of your mission, for example, student, teacher, talk show host, artist. So long as you see the connection to an overriding plan, you can fill these roles with minimal stress and confusion.

There is a special place for you in the universe. Realize that place by accessing, affirming, accepting and applying your mission. You are uniquely qualified to carry out this task. In fact, you are charged with the responsibility of expressing and manifesting your specific mission.

5) Mission and Passion

A mission is strongly connected to our collective passions. You can live an enthusiastic life by consistently connecting to your personal mission. In so doing, you will use your energy wisely and effectively in the service of your soul's purpose.

6) Mission and Abundance

We heartily embrace abundance and the principles of prosperity. Following a mission does not guarantee that you will enjoy immediate monetary reward. Sometimes hardship and challenges are a necessary part of the mission path. But you will eventually prosper and have the things you desire to the degree that you desire them. You will also thrive in a spiritual sense. Right action brings right reward.

Some form of prosperity will manifest; it may take the form of money, time, space, serenity, freedom, creativity—or a true friend in whom you can confide your innermost dreams. Following your mission manifests a happiness no amount of money can buy. Material wealth won't matter unless the way you live your life matters.

Getting the most from this Workbook

The approach and exercises in this book are based on Life Mission Associates' experience with individual clients, workshop participants and readers. Space is provided in the workbook for you to complete the exercises. The format is deliberately directive and systematic. Occasionally, we'll give you field work to do. These field projects will require additional time to be worked through. Don't rush to complete them. They are designed to accompany, but not interrupt, the work you do on the page.

For best results, devote your time and energy to doing all exercises in a consistent manner. "Suit up/dress up and show up" is the term used in twelve step programs. Work the principles and exercises of this workbook faithfully and you will:

1) Identify your strengths, resources and passions.
2) Link these assets with an overall sense of purpose.
3) Translate this purpose into a specific mission.
4) Apply your mission to multiple aspects of your life.
5) Align your day-to-day goals with that mission.
6) Do only that which matches your true desires.
7) Identify and overcome blocks to true self-fulfillment.
8) Find a realistic platform for your mission.
9) Transfer your mission into sustained, committed action.
10) Affirm and maintain your right path.

The Three P'S and the Three C'S

Any mission, large or small, requires thoughtful preparation for successful completion. We encourage you, therefore, to practice "The Three P's:" planning, preparation, and positioning. As any farmer knows, you need proper planning, preparation, and positioning for a successful crop. When you apply The Three P's, you decide what you want, plant the seeds, nurture and feed your mission process and then harvest the fruits of your work. Growth is guaranteed with this method.

The Three P's are sustained by The Three C's: caring, commitment, and consistency. You don't have to do all of the exercises at once. Simply commit to doing them regularly with love and devotion. If you work on a consistent basis at least 15 minutes a day, it will net you far more than spending one sporadic hour every now and then. This work can best be done in the privacy of your own home.

Make the process as pleasant as possible by doing the following:

1) Put yourself in a supportive, pleasing surrounding.
2) Give yourself breaks for maximum energy.
3) Do your exercises at a high energy point of the day.
4) Work in as relaxed and peaceful a manner as possible.
5) Remember that results come when they need to and not necessarily according to *your* timetable.
6) Release the process after you have laid the groundwork.

The Structure of this Workbook

Think of this workbook as a treasure hunt divided into seven parts or modules. Each module covers one phase of the life mission search and takes you deeper and deeper until you find the treasure buried within—your mission. The final module helps you put that mission into action.

Gathering Clues

The most important operative principle of the book is that a mission is comprised of clues, which are put together, (like pieces of a puzzle) to form your mission picture. As each piece is added, a pattern begins to emerge, and you move closer to seeing the complete picture.

We have provided a Clue Section at the back of this workbook for you to list all clues derived from exercises. When you write down a clue, don't worry about its individual meaning for now. Even if it may not seem like much, it contributes to the total mission. Likewise, refrain from overinterpreting a clue. Its meaning will become easier after your have collected a number of them on one page.

The process of gathering clues flows as follows:

exercises > clues > patterns > picture > meaning > insight

Mission Journal

We recommend using a separate journal to record any private thoughts, comments, responses to exercises, daily events, prose writing, pictures, articles from newspapers, encouraging quotes— anything that occurs to you at times when you are not working in this book. It's fun to decorate the outside of your journal and give it your own personalized title. Summarize the insights recorded in your journal and transfer them to the Clue Section.

Mission Buddy

Call someone you trust to support you and ask this person to be your "mission buddy." For best results, call your buddy every day before you begin an exercise or task. Call this person again after you complete the work. Someday you can return the favor by becoming someone else's mission buddy.

Mission and Recovery

Remember that you are probably recovering from years of self-avoidance. You may have given your energy to self-defeating thoughts, societal myths, and other people's desires or agendas. You may have put everything else before your mission.

You may have engaged in compulsive activities involving food, sex, drugs, alcohol or work that are incompatible with your mission goals. Finding your life mission can help you recover from any self-defeating addictions. Working this book may be the first step in proving to yourself that you have power over your life. Success is about to begin!

Mission and You

Each reader starts this journey in a different place. Some of you may know what your mission is, but you seek validation. Some of you may feel lost and unclear. Others of you may fear taking the steps necessary to realize your mission. Wherever your point of departure may be, we welcome you to this process. You are not alone on this journey. You have a source within you that will give you strength if you ask for it. Make use of buddies, counseling and support groups as necessary. Or form a Life Mission support group yourself!

We at *Life Mission Associates* are only a phone call away at (704) 298-8003 (office), or (800) 957-8888 (message line). Please contact us with feedback or questions, or for further help. We want you to succeed, and we want your mission to be gloriously possible. All aboard!

MODULE ONE:
Taking Stock

Every successful business needs a solid inventory of stocks and assets. Likewise, the process of finding your life mission requires proper and careful inventory of your talents, skills, experiences, strengths and gifts.

The purpose of Module One is to:

1) Survey your feelings before beginning this process.
2) Generate material that will serve as building blocks for your mission.
3) Identify your areas of expertise.
4) Determine the influences in your life.

1.01 *Where I am Now*

First, let's take an emotional inventory. Starting on a new path can be scary, exciting, frightening or, perish the thought, just plain fun! Each person comes to this process with different feelings. It's important to be totally honest about your emotional state as you begin this journey. Some days you may feel like opening this workbook, other days you may not. That's normal. Until you feel comfortable with the process, it may be a good idea to do "Where I am Now" each day before you begin.

1. As I start this process, I feel

ANXIOUS, yet hopeful & Curious and wanting answers to this question - what is my calling, my purpose; why am I here (on Earth) ?

2. The way I prefer to do this work is

Slowly because it takes deep thought & "mood" interferes hence time and frame of mind is needed. I also feel very private about my thoughts - at least until I'm confident about the direction & feel more self-directed in this process.

3. If I am discouraged or reluctant, I'll help myself by

Allowing myself to push through beyond the muck.

1.02 *My Emotional Warm Spot*

(See pp. 160-162 in FYSP)

As you complete the various assignments in this workbook, it helps to find or create a comfortable place where you can work without distraction.

Your emotional warm spot (EWS) is that favorite place in or around your childhood home where you felt good and safe. It served as your getaway, retreat, or place of nurturing. Even if your family moved a lot, or if you had a difficult childhood, or didn't have much space to yourself, you probably had one spot where you could find solace and get centered.

Maybe your EWS was in a tree, an attic, a garage, an alcove, a bedroom or a kitchen. Wherever, it was a place you could just be yourself. By remembering your EWS, you access information about the type of environment in which you felt safe to be yourself.

Write about how you felt in this space—not the negative feelings that may have driven you there—but the positive feelings you experienced while you were there. What did you do when you were in your EWS? Did you think? Read? Talk to a real or imaginary person? Who was that person? What were they doing while you were there? How long did you usually stay in your EWS? How often did you go there? Write about your EWS here:

I guess it was my bedroom – its wasn't always private but often I could make it so when I grew older... When the rm was mine alone (some of my teen yrs) My "things" surrounded me. My bed was comfortable & safe. I remember my shrine & the area off the chicken coop was a place to be un viewed & alone. Remember my Daddy's work room?! And then Nacio's House...

Your EWS provided an opportunity for fantasy and escape as well as a creative environment for generating ideas and solving problems. You may have lost the actual physical connection with your old EWS, but you can always find another one.

1.03 *My Experience with this Workbook*

Many feelings, both positive and negative, will come up for you while doing the work in this book. Typical reactions to the exercises in this book may include euphoria and hope that you are starting on an adventure, antagonism toward a particular exercise, overwhelming feelings of frustration from what seems to be a daunting task, or discomfort from doing something that you think may exceed your present emotional capabilities. Maybe you dislike someone else telling you what to do. Whatever your response to any part of this book, be sure that you are aware of it. Repeat this exercise whenever you need to review your emotional state.

1. I bought this workbook because

I want to know. And this book furnished a journey - a path :

2. When I reach the end of this workbook, my hope is that

I will know why I'm here.

3. When I finish this workbook, I fear that

4. When the going gets tough, I will help myself by

1.04 *You are not alone in this Process*

It is important to recognize those who may lend you support during your journey. You have friends, family members, mates, co-workers, neighbors and buddies who know you are on a quest. How much you decide to let them in on the process is an individual decision. In this module you will examine your support system and how you intend to use it.

Who believes in you? Who might resist if you start asserting yourself and taking charge? Who can you call on for support when you feel down and discouraged? Whom do you want to be privy to this process from the start? Who will go along with your mission no matter what? In short, who can turn to for cheerleading, mentoring, guidance, and coaching?

I can always count on the following people to be there for me:

Karobe

Sharon

My Reiki Guides & higher self

Some of your support people can offer personal help or professional help. Some people you can call just to talk. Others can review what you've written. Other friends might help with field projects or run errands for you when things get hectic. What kind of help do you need?

I need help from my support network in the following ways:

1.05 *Assisters and Resisters*

Fieldwork:

Create a place that is similar to your original EWS. For example, if you climbed a tree, find another tree near your work place or home that inspires the same warm feeling. Spend time near the tree on a regular basis. You may be inspired to write in the workbook in your new spot. Pay attention to the thoughts and feelings you have while in this EWS, and record any insights or clues in your Clue Section.

We Homo Sapiens are seldom alone in any endeavor. We are all part of a human web, social critters who care about what others think—especially by those we are closest to. But, some of those people may hinder us rather than help us along this path. Who might you feel uncomfortable involving in this process right now? Who might resist or resent your success? These are NOT people you want to call upon now.

I plan to leave the following people OUT of my plans right now:

_____

_____

_____

because

_____

_____

_____

_____

_____

1.06 *Commitment to Yourself*

Regardless of how much support you get from others, you must be your own best friend in this process. Make a pact with yourself to persevere no matter what distractions, doubts, fears, sadness, depression or time constraints get in your way. Only you know the realistic limits of your capacity for daily work; by making an agreement with yourself on paper you can keep moving forward.

Commitment Contract:

Name __Mary Olivia Piper__

Date __Jan. 31, 2003__

1. I commit to work _____ minutes a day on this book for _____ days a week.

2. If I miss a day, I plan to

_____

_____

_____

3. If my original estimate isn't comfortable for me, I'll make the following adjustments:

_____

_____

_____

4. I'll create a safe space for myself to work by

_____

_____

_____

5. If I get stuck, I'll

_____

_____

_____

6. Each time I complete a task, I'll reward myself by

_____

_____

_____

1.07 *Me and my Mission*

Examine your feelings about the term Life Mission. It's important to acknowledge both negative as well as positive attitudes. Check the statements that apply to you:

☐ I know what my mission is.

☐ I know what my mission is, but I'm not sure how to make it happen.

☐ I don't know what my mission is.

☑ I don't think I'll ever find out what my mission is.

☐ I know what I like, but I'm not sure how to create a mission out of it.

☐ I don't know if I'll like my mission once I find it.

☐ I trust the Life Mission process.

☐ I'm afraid I'll lose interest in my mission after a while.

☐ I'm afraid I won't have enough talent to fulfill my mission.

☑ I believe everyone has a mission.

☐ I'm afraid my friends/relatives/family of origin will not approve of my mission.

Summarize your own definition of what mission means to you.

To me, mission means:

_____

_____

_____

_____

_____

_____

_____

_____

1.08 *My Mission Secrets*

Is there something that you have always wanted to manifest—something that you've never admitted to anyone? It's time to admit your secret desires, doubts, and fears to yourself. By keeping secrets from yourself or others, you hold back on your mission quest.

What is the secret that you are holding back? What do you want that nobody knows about? How has keeping this desire a secret affected your life? What are you afraid will happen if you make your secret known? Maybe you fear that your secret desire will conflict with your family's desires.

For example, it may be that you've spent your life striving to be number one. You're ambitious, competitive, and you've climbed every mountain placed in front of you. But now you want to lead a less driven, more satisfying life in the slow lane. To admit that you want out of the rat race may be difficult, but you've got to take the pressure off of yourself in order to switch lanes and pursue a mission based on desire.

My secret desire is:

_____

_____

_____

_____

_____

_____

_____

_____

1.09 *Brag List*

Talents, too, can be buried or not admitted. List your sterling qualities, traits, skills, talents, and characteristics—a positive repertoire describing yourself. It's brag time. There is no need to be shy or reserved. This is also an expandable list. Get a flip chart so that you can add to it daily. Ask others to add colorful descriptions.

_____

_____

_____

_____

_____

_____

_____

By using this brag list, you can analyze your chief sources of strength. What internal resources do you draw upon when the chips are down? What resources do you use daily? What stands you in good stead no matter what?

At the end of each day, conduct a short review. What skills have you drawn upon during the day? What strengths did you neglect or use infrequently?

Skills I Used Today

_____

_____

_____

_____

Skills I Neglected Today

_____

_____

_____

_____

Choose one skill that you could practice more consistently, and describe how you intend to use it in the next 24 hours.

_____

_____

_____

_____

1.10 *Messages from Parents*

The greatest influences on your life direction most likely came from your parents or care givers. Many of us still have feelings of anger, disappointment, and sadness about our parents' or guardian's advice. We may also have feelings of love, caring and affection about the guidance that they gave us.

If you received messages like the following examples, your parents may have unconsciously wanted you to pursue their missions rather than your own.

- No Dexter kid is ever going to be an artist.
- Girls should prepare themselves for marriage by studying liberal arts.
- Law is the only decent profession for a male in this family.

Your parents' prejudices may also have influenced your choices. If racist statements were common in your household, you might have thought twice about your desire to join the Peace Corps and serve in Africa. If your parents maligned homosexuals, you might have adopted a lifestyle inappropriate for your sexual orientation.

a) Take time to write about your parental influences here. How did their messages directly influence your choice of hobbies, careers, jobs, college major, lifestyle, or mate?

_____

_____

_____

_____

_____

_____

_____

b) Now, write a sentence or two that describes the way your mother and father and other significant people wanted you to lead your life. Even if they never said it in so many words, you absorbed the idea through mental suggestion. Use their language or style of communicating to complete the following as though they were addressing you directly.

Message from my father:

_____

_____

_____

_____

Message from my mother:

_____

_____

_____

_____

Messages from relatives or other care givers:

_____

_____

_____

_____

My feelings about the advice they gave me:

_____

_____

_____

_____

1.11 *Family Lessons*

Remember this paradoxical truth about mission: although it is an individual matter, unique to you, it takes shape within a broader context. For instance, your family of origin helped shape your understanding of certain truths about your own destiny.

What important, valid and positive lessons did you learn about life as a result of having your particular care givers or family? What things were you able to learn only from that environment? What unique qualities did you develop as a result?

_____

_____

_____

_____

_____

_____

_____

_____

_____

_____

_____

_____

_____

_____

1.12 *Influential People in my Life*

It is valuable to get clear about the direction you have taken in response to other influential people in your life, such as teachers, friends, mates, bosses, and colleagues. Name a key person in your life. What, in a nutshell, was his or her most influential message to you? What choices did you make (good or bad) that were influenced by this person? Use an additional sheet of paper to repeat this exercise as many times as you wish.

A key person in my life was

_____

_____

His/her message to me:

_____

_____

_____

_____

_____

Under his/her influence, I made the following choice(s):

_____

_____

_____

_____

_____

1.13 *Cultural Influences*

You are influenced by the cultural contexts and the era in which you grew up; the place of origin and ethnic or religious background firmly sets the climate for your belief systems. If you had been born in Russia in 1938, for example, how might your life have been different? Write about your own background here:

Being born in (race, culture)_____

_____ in

(year)_____ has impacted me in the following ways:

_____

_____

_____

_____

_____

_____

_____

_____

_____

_____

_____

_____

_____

_____

1.14 *I am a Resource*

There is a relationship between your mission and what you enjoy, what you are adept at, or what you know a lot about. A mission gives you the means to express all of your aptitudes and strengths.

Write down as many as five subjects, or areas of knowledge, or skills in which you have some level of expertise.

Examples: I am a resource for

- learning to read computer manuals
- teaching beginning piano
- getting around Los Angeles without using the freeway
- traveling in the Czech Republic
- inventing word games

Now it's your turn:
I am a resource for:

_____

_____

_____

_____

_____

Other people can give us clues about our mission strengths. Ask others about your areas of expertise. What kind of assistance do people come to you for? What do they ask you about? Why do they call you or associate with you? Even the questions a stranger might ask you on the street can be enlightening. This information will stimulate insights about yourself and provide further clues to add to your inventory.

Others consider me a resource for the following:

_____

_____

_____

_____

_____

Fieldwork:

As you work on this exercise, pay close attention to whatever makes your interest level rise when you talk about a subject. Do this for at least a week.

31

1.15 *Achievements*

Which specific achievements are you most proud of? They can be humble or huge events in your life. For example, did you complete your education while working part time? Did you paint your house by yourself? Did you successfully raise money for the local girls' club? List five achievements here:

_____

_____

_____

_____

_____

Continue by analyzing your achievements as follows:

1. The achievement I am most proud of is:

_____

_____

2. I felt good about it because

_____

_____

_____

_____

3. This achievement reveals to me that I

_____

_____

_____

This exercise can be repeated for each achievement you listed.

Transfer any insights to your Clue Section.

1.16 *Just a Minute*

Answering questions at rapid fire can bring insights. Quickly respond to the following questions as clearly and concisely as you can. Spend only one minute on each question.

1) What was the high point of your day yesterday?

_____

_____

Last week ?

_____

_____

Last month?

_____

_____

Last year?

_____

_____

Ever?

_____

_____

2) If you were given $200,000 to do whatever you wanted for a year, what would you do?

_____

_____

_____

_____

3) What is the most adventurous thing you have ever done?

_____

_____

_____

_____

4) If you could be anyone on the planet, who would you be? Why?

_____

_____

_____

_____

5) If you had an extra five minutes of awake time per day, what would you use it for?

_____

_____

_____

_____

6) Off the top of your head, list four improvements that you would like to see happen in the world, but for which you do not have to take responsibility—(e.g., newspaper print that doesn't rub off on your hands, run-resistant nylons, a cure for cancer).

_____

_____

_____

_____

7) Imagine that you are on a plane, and you find yourself seated next to someone that you have always wanted to meet. Who would it be? What would you talk about?

_____

_____

_____

_____

8) If you could live your life over, what would you change? Why?

_____

_____

_____

_____

Module One Review Questions

1. What are my hopes, fears and thoughts concerning my mission?

_____

_____

_____

_____

_____

2. What is my EWS today? How can I use it to get insights and ideas?

_____

_____

_____

_____

3. Who is part of my mission support system?

_____

_____

_____

4. What persons do I wish to exclude from that system for now?

_____

_____

_____

5. What specifically is my time commitment to my mission?

_____

_____

_____

6. How have family and cultural influences affected my mission?

_____

_____

_____

_____

_____

7. How do my resources give me clues about my current interests and desires?

_____

_____

_____

_____

_____

8. What are my primary achievements? Which can I use more often in my Life Mission search?

_____

_____

_____

_____

_____

_____

_____

MODULE TWO:
You Have a Dream

"I have a dream!" Martin Luther King declared in his stirring oratory during the 1963 March on Washington. The authors resonate with that statement, because we believe that everyone has a dream. We define a dream as a yet-to-be-fulfilled desire, a "goal," a "wish" or a project that you have deferred.

We may be doing our utmost to fulfill that dream, but so often, we let it languish within our hearts. This module will show you how to translate your dream into reality.

All glorious achievements of humankind, life-saving inventions, beautiful music and art, started as ideas or dreams in someone's heart and mind. A mission is a collection or composite of many smaller dreams—what we referred to earlier as a "string of pearls." When you learn to manifest one of your dreams, you'll be able to repeat the process and string them together. The collective dreams in your string of pearls will help define your mission. In this module, you will learn to do the following:

1) Identify a specific dream.
2) Assess resources for making your dream possible.
3) Take specific steps to manifest your dream.
4) Access the part of you which harbors the dream.
5) Apply this model to every dream in your mission search.

2.01 *To Dream the Possible Dream*

Some people are blocked from fulfilling their dreams because they are afraid it will be impossible to manifest them. They may even deny that they have any hopes or desires. In *Alice in Wonderland*, Alice tells the queen that she doesn't believe impossible things. The queen replies that she practices believing at least six impossible things a day before breakfast, and that all one needs is practice. If you, like the queen, will practice imagining the fulfillment of your dreams, you can manifest them!

List one goal or desire, big or small, that you are prepared to believe is possible for you to attain, if only for this exercise. Choose something that gnaws at you because you haven't completed it— something that tugs at your heartstrings. Make it a dream that you truly want to manifest. You're going to use this exercise as a model for manifesting other dreams.

Here are some specific guidelines for writing down your dream:

1) Limit the dream to one desire, such as, " I want to paint," or "I want to sculpt."

2) Make the dream specific. " I want to paint landscapes in the Loire Valley."

3) Make fulfillment of the dream measurable so you will know whether or not you have achieved it. " I want to be happy" is vague. What does happiness mean to you? If you define it as living in Tuscany, then you should phrase it: "My dream is to live in a small village in Tuscany by the year 2005." Here you have a dream which is specific and measurable.

Some examples of specific dreams:
- My dream is to earn a B.A. in art history from my local university in three years.
- My dream is to plant a rose garden in my backyard.
- My dream is to meet the President of the United States.
- My dream is to trace my mother's family tree back to 1750.

My dream is to

_____

_____

_____

2.02 *Manifesting your Dream*

Now you'll work on manifesting your dream. Your job is to believe in your dream. How do you begin doing that? As the queen rightly stated, you have to practice! Let's look at ways you can move your dream from the impossible to the possible.

Think of all the resources that you have to fulfill your dream: your background, education, technical training, skills, hobbies, finances, friends, contacts, parents, or practical experience. Let's say your dream is to go to the next Olympic Games. Your list of resources might read like this:

- I like track (or swimming, or horses).
- I have traveled throughout Europe and the United States.
- I have taken a year of foreign language.
- I have $1000 in a savings account.
- I once led a tour of high school students to Europe.

Fieldwork:

Inspire yourself by looking at other people's realized dreams— the lamp you read by, the design of your home, a baseball field nearby. All these began as someone's dream.

2.03 *Being Resourceful*

List any of your resources (including any from exercise 1.14) which directly relate to, or can be used in the service of your dream.

My resource list:

_____

_____

_____

_____

_____

Share your resource list with three friends and have them add to it:

_____

_____

_____

2.04 *Show and (Don't) Tell*

Show your dream to these three people. Ask them to write down their reaction to your dream in one concise sentence. Do not tell them how you feel about your dream. Transfer their responses to this workbook.

First Person's Response:

_____

_____

_____

Second Person's Response:

_____

_____

_____

Third Person's Response:

_____

_____

_____

Summarize your friends' reactions to your dream here. Did they believe that your dreams were possible or impossible? Did they laugh, ridicule, or express reservations about your dream? Were you surprised by their responses?

_____

_____

_____

_____

_____

2.05 *Dipping into the Past*

You can be your own greatest inspiration! You have probably already done what you've dreamed of—in some similar way. We call that similarity a past equivalent. Look at your dream, see a key ingredient that is needed to accomplish it, and look to your past to see if you have done something equivalent.

Maybe your dream is to become the first woman in your family to head your own company. A key ingredient is leadership ability. Think back to an event in your past where you were in charge. Did you lead a girl scout troop? Were you a Sunday School teacher? Were you Valedictorian of your high school class? Have you been an officer of a club?

Here are some examples of dreams, a key ingredient, and a past equivalent

Dream I	Ingredient	Past Equivalent
To be president of my company	leadership	Was Vice-President of Chemistry Club in H.S.
To own my own home	ownership / responsibility	Bought my own car at age 17
To speak French	speak foreign language	Learned German in high school

Now you fill in the ingredients and equivalent to your present dream.

My dream	Ingredient	Past Equivalent
_____	_____	_____
_____	_____	_____
_____	_____	_____

How you could transfer this past equivalent to your key ingredient and thus realize your dream?

_____

_____

_____

2.06 *Beautiful Dreamers*

Another way of making your dreams possible is to examine the lives of others who have manifested things which are similar to your dream. If you'd like to be the first woman in your family to run a business, do some research. Find women at the helm of companies. Do you want to have your book published? Well, 90,000 books a year get published. A lot of people turn their dream into reality! Find an example that matches your dream.

Example:

My Dream:	*Equivalent Things Done by Someone Else:*
To head my own company	Ms. Jones, head of XYZ, Inc.
To write a book about snails	A college friend wrote a book about lizards.

Now it's your turn:

My Dream:	*Equivalent Things Done By Someone Else:*
_____	_____
_____	_____
_____	_____

2.07 *Getting a Transfer: Just ask for it*

Think of a project you completed in the past that is similar to your current dream. List everything that you did to enable you to accomplish that goal. These skills are transferable! Determine which related skills you could recycle to realize your present dream.

Example:
My dream: To give a public speech on creative gardening to local organizations. Previous related project: Acted in college play.

What I did:

- searched catalogues or area schools for class
- enrolled in acting class I liked
- watched more movies and plays than normal
- did my assignments

- went to rehearsals every week
- learned my lines

How It can transfer:

- find local groups wanting speaker
- attend group meeting
- listen to other public speakers
- read a book on public speaking
- practice speech in front of friends
- rehearse my speech techniques

Your Turn:

My dream:

_____

_____

_____

_____

Previous related project:

_____

_____

_____

_____

What I did:

_____

_____

_____

_____

How it can transfer:

_____

_____

_____

_____

2.08 *Reality Check: What am I doing for my Dream?*

Numerous goals need to be met in order to fulfill a dream. These goals are fed by daily accomplishments. But not every daily accomplishment relates to your goal. The key is intention. Does your intention for the accomplishment further your goal or dream? Here's the way it works. Let's say that your goal is to make a certain number of real estate sales. In order to achieve your quota, you must escort clients around in your car. You want to make a good impression, so washing the car is a necessary step in the service of this goal.

task > intention > accomplishment > goal > dream

clean car > impress client > get sale > earn enough money > go to Paris

Caveat: Not every time you wash your car does it serve a higher goal! Here is a reality check for practice. You want to assess whether your intention furthers your dream. Write down your dream and three things that you have accomplished this week.

Dream: To go to the next Olympics
   Three things I accomplished this week:
   1) cleaning out my files
   2) getting the Jones account straightened out
   3) talking to Aunt Mary

Do these goals relate to the dream? Let's look:

Accomplishment	*Assessment of Intention*	
Cleaned out office files	Helped me get organized and find my passport	YES
Straightened out Jones account	Got me a raise, enabled me to afford trip	YES
Talked to Aunt Mary	Asked about her visit to 1976 Olympics, gathered info	YES

Strive for rigorous honesty in assessing your intention when you list accomplishments. No fudging! The intention MUST relate in some way to furthering the goal/dream. Without an honest intention, give that task a NO. Sometimes a simple question to yourself.

"Why did I do this?" will uncover the intention. Consider the following assessment of the same accomplishments.

Accomplishment:	Assessment of Intention:	
Cleaned out office files	Done out of frustration to avoid sales calls	NO
Straightened out Jones account	Should have been done by colleague	NO
Talked to Aunt Mary	Discussed family problems	NO

Transfer your dream from exercise 2.01:

_____

_____

In the left column, list as many as ten tasks that you completed in the last seven days. (i.e., finished reading a book, sent in a tax form, got an airline reservation, picked out paint for child's room). Then assess each item for your intention; notice how it relates to your goal or dream. Give each item a YES or a NO.

Accomplishment:	Assessment of Intention:	Yes	No
_____	_____	☐	☐
_____	_____	☐	☐
_____	_____	☐	☐
_____	_____	☐	☐
_____	_____	☐	☐
_____	_____	☐	☐
_____	_____	☐	☐
_____	_____	☐	☐
_____	_____	☐	☐
_____	_____	☐	☐

How many of your accomplishments were related to your dream? If you spend time on things that have no bearing on your goals, ask yourself why.

Studies have shown that one out of nine accomplishments directly relate to a person's overall life goal. Even if your ratio is four out of nine, you are blocking yourself more than 50% of the time by engaging in activities that are not related to your goals.

2.09 *Do Dream vs. Day Dream*

Here's how to increase the ratio between intentions, accomplishments, and goals. List three things that you will do this week which directly relate to your goals and dreams. Be sure your intention harmonizes with the accomplishment of your dream.

Things I Will Do: *How It Relates to My Dream:*

_____   _____

_____   _____

_____   _____

What can you do in the next 24 hours that directly relates to manifesting your dream?

_____

_____

_____

_____

2.10 *Seeing is Believing*

Sometimes your dream needs dramatization. Visualize yourself acting out your dream. If you were actually living your dream, how would you feel, think, or be? Describe:

_____

_____

_____

_____

_____

_____

2.11 *Goal beyond the Goal*

Support your daily accomplishments by visualizing yourself receiving benefits from your completed dream. For example, if your dream is to go to France, visualize yourself speaking French, looking at vacation pictures with friends, driving the car that you rented in Europe, or talking with a friend you made there. Concentrate on the outcome of your dream. Act as if it has already happened and you are now enjoying the fruits of your efforts. List the outcomes associated with your dream here.

_____

_____

_____

_____

_____

2.12 *Grabbing yourself by the Tale*

Fairy tales and dreams have much in common. A fairy tale is a collective dream that society wants to believe (Cinderella, Snow White, Hansel and Gretel). Now you have a chance to create your own fairy tale—one that YOU can believe in.

By casting your dream into a fairy tale, you are able to see your dream from another angle. It's also creative and fun! (This method was used effectively in *The One Minute Manager*.) Write a fairy tale about yourself as you would like your life to be. You can use an actual fairy tale, or change an existing tale to fit your fantasy, or make up one from scratch. Use simple children's vocabulary to write your tale.

My Dream written as a Fairy Tale:
    Once upon a time, there was

_____

_____

_____

_____

_____

_____

_____

_____

_____

_____

_____

_____

_____

_____

_____

Jot down any insights that you had from writing this fairy tale. Concentrate on what you fantasized about, and how this fantasy relates to your mission.

_____

_____

_____

_____

_____

_____

_____

_____

Module Two Review Questions:

1. What kinds of new ideas did I get about manifesting dreams?

_____

_____

_____

_____

2. What can I do to make a dream possible?

_____

_____

_____

_____

3. How did feedback help me revise my opinion of my dream?

_____

_____

_____

_____

4. What resources do I have that I was previously unaware of?

_____

_____

_____

_____

5. What have I done that is similar to my dream?

_____

_____

_____

_____

6. What ways can I incorporate my dream into my life now?

_____

_____

_____

_____

7. How much of what I have accomplished now relates to the dream that I have identified?

_____

_____

_____

_____

8. What perks would I enjoy as a result of realizing my dream?

_____

_____

_____

_____

9. What insights did I get from my fairy tale work?

_____

_____

_____

_____

MODULE THREE:
Overcoming Blocks, Barriers, and Boundaries

In this module you will identify and devise strategies to overcome personal barriers, blocks and boundaries that prevent you from seeking your mission. In Module Two you identified a dream and the resources that you have to manifest your dream. While you practiced the exercises in Module Two, you may have noticed feelings of resistance, doubt and objection. This is your chance to grapple with those negative reactions and evaluate them objectively.

3.01 *The Impossible Dream*

Rewrite your dream from page 38 here.

My dream:

_____

_____

Now, list any reasons that block you from accomplishing this dream.

_____

_____

_____

_____

Personal barriers, blocks and boundaries (the three B's) are distinguishable from real obstacles and limitations. Blocks are internal—your own "stuff"—and are therefore different from actual obstacles. The lack of finances, physical disabilities, or poor market conditions are all examples of external obstacles. Distinguishing between the two can be tricky, since your perceptions, habits and attitudes profoundly affect how you define reality.

For the sake of clarity, we have divided internal blocks into three categories: cognitive, emotional, and behavioral.

COGNITIVE BLOCKS

Cognitive blocks are self-statements or programmed ideas that we often receive from well-meaning (and sometimes not-so-well meaning) family members, friends, co-workers, and teachers. We may also make them up ourselves. These ideas are fixed and powerfully influence our thinking, our behavior and our lives. Cognitive blocks are the result of negative thinking. They are "negations," as opposed to affirmations; they are compelling agents that change the outcome of an event to correspond with your assessment of the situation.

One type of cognitive block discussed in FYSP is the "idea killer." Idea killers are statements made without thinking, almost by habit, they can prevent us from even considering an idea, let alone testing it. Idea killers are often negative self-talk so that we won't have to follow through with a dream. For example: "I can't write." or "Nobody would ever hire a 50-year-old to perform in a night club."

Whatever the negation, you can be sure that it involves a strongly held assumption.

Other Examples of Idea Killers:

I'm too old.
It's too late.
There's no market for my talents.
It's been tried before.
It won't work.
My mate, partner, family won't approve.

Here are some Idea Killers you may have heard others say to you:

Do something practical!
What makes you think you can do that?
You'll never make a living if you study art.
No daughter of mine is going to drive a motorcycle.
If it's good enough for Aunt Lizzy, it's good enough for you.
Where do you get all those weird ideas?
But you've invested all that money in your degree!

You may not even be aware of these "implants," which Eric Berne refers to as "tapes." These "implants" need to be teased out and identified so that they can be transformed or reprogrammed. This process is something like psychological surgery. Be alert for the implanted tapes that mentally obstruct the path to your mission. Review the reasons that you listed for thinking that you can't fulfill your dream. Which ideas are blocks and which ideas are real obstacles?

3.02 *Getting Rid of Idea Killers*

One way to counter cognitive blocks is to rework negative thinking by using affirmations. Any idea killer can be turned into a positive statement. Here's how:

- identify negative statements
- challenge them
- get fresh data
- rephrase negative statements

1. Think of a task that you never seem to complete: paying bills, writing a letter, or calling a difficult person. What idea killers do you use to keep yourself from finishing the task?

Task:

_____

_____

Idea killers:

a. _____

b. _____

c. _____

2. Challenge one of the statements you listed above. Look for exaggerations, generalizations, or assumptions. How would you respond if somebody else said such a thing to you?

Example: I'm too old to go back to college.
Retort: How old is too old? What subject are you too old to understand?

Humor is another way to diffuse negative thinking.

Example: Women aren't good at math.
Retort: Do people study math with their genitals?

Your Idea Killer:_____

Retort:_____

Your Idea Killer: _____

Retort: _____

Your Idea Killer: _____

Retort: _____

This mental exercise may seem a bit contrived at first. But when you realize your negative statements are just as contrived, you can begin to revise them.

3. Negative thinking flourishes in mental darkness. One way to combat darkness is by gathering information and fresh data. Do some reading that challenges your negative statements. Ask around—talk to people who have overcome their negative assumptions. New information can be a powerful weapon against negative thinking.

4. Rephrase any of your negative statements, even if you don't believe the affirming statement.
(You might find a good sources for negation in your dream section where you listed blocks.)

Example:

Old Negative Statement:	*New Affirming Statement:*
I'm too old to return to school.	I'm looking forward to returning to school.
I don't have enough money to go to the Olympics.	I can save $20 a week for the Olympics.

Old Negative Statements:	*New Affirming Statements:*
_____	_____
_____	_____
_____	_____
_____	_____

Use at least one of your new affirming statements this week just after you catch yourself using an old negative one.
Tip: apply your rephrasing technique to the negative statement that bugs you most.

3.03 *I Think Positive, Therefore I Do*

Now, we'll turn to the good stuff—positive statements. Spontaneously list a project that you completed in spite of any obstacles.

Examples:
- helped my daughter understand the present perfect tense in German
- taught myself how to rewire a lamp
- organized the homeless to clean up a prospective shelter

Your example:

_____

How did you encourage yourself to get through the process?

_____

_____

How can you apply your successful methods and self-statements to a project that you're presently blocked on?

I can _____

_____

3.04 *Self-Fulfilling Prophecy*

The self-fulfilling prophecy can be one big dream killer. This is the disease of "equationitis". It goes something like this: "If I leave my job for something I love, I'll never earn as much money as I do now." The underlying message is this: "If I do what I love, I'll be poor." The equation is: loving my work = poverty.

Think of something for which you have predicted the outcome. Write down that predicted outcome, and the equation which underlies your thinking.

Statement	*My Predicted Outcome*	*Equation*
_____ >	_____ =	_____

To remove the block and take action, recast the old equation into a positive goal.

Old equation:	Positive Goal:
Loving my work = poverty	If I do what I love, I'll be healthy, happy and fulfilled

Recast your old equations here:

Old Equation:	Positive Goal:
_____	_____
_____	_____
_____	_____

EMOTIONAL BLOCKS

Emotions are part of a fine-tuned, self-guidance system that causes us to react with aversion to that which hurts us and with pleasure and happiness toward that which sustains and nurtures us. Fear of fire is healthy because it keeps us from being burned. Grief is a natural emotion too; it helps us let go of a beloved person or object. Anger helps us preserve integrity and boundaries. Healthy joy and excitement leads us into activities that are congruent with our nature (our mission path).

Emotions are trained, shaped and modified by the dominant culture and family patterns. Unfortunately, many of us who were subjected to hostile, critical or repressive parenting have become estranged from our emotions and are so traumatized and stressed that we became emotionally blocked.

How do we tell when we may be dealing with emotional blocks? When we can't seem to do what we want, when we avoid situations or people because they make us uncomfortable, and when we stumble on our mission path or sabotage ourselves. Unresolved grief over a lost opportunity, resentment toward an interfering parent or spouse, and fear of success or abandonment are all emotions that can block us in our mission work.

3.05 *Acknowledging Blocks to your Dreams*

List the emotional blocks that are holding you back from manifesting a dream. Express your feelings; you may have to dig deeper for them. Identify all emotion words and underline them.

Example:

My dream is to go to the next Olympic Games.

Emotional Blocks:

I'm afraid to travel without my mate.
Leaving my children would make me too sad.
I resent my parents for not encouraging me to develop my athletic abilities.

Some emotional blocks to my dream include: _____

_____

_____

_____

_____

_____

_____

_____

_____

_____

_____

_____

_____

3.06 *Good Grief!*

Unacknowledged grief is a common block to fulfilling dreams. We often delay action because we're afraid to tap into deep-seated sadness. Maybe you are at mid-life and have always wanted to dance but never have. Perhaps you blew a chance to study in Europe. Or maybe you entered into a relationship instead of going to college. You may be saying to yourself, "What a fool I've been, passing up all those experiences."

Instead of blaming yourself, grieve for any missed opportunities. Identify, accept, and feel your inevitable sadness. Then, and only then, can you put the loss behind you and move on to current reality. Writing is a good way to pave a path to the present. What do you mourn not doing? If you had your life to live over, what would you change? How would that feel? How do you feel about letting go of what you cannot retrieve? Concentrate on your feelings of mourning, sadness, regret and grief. Admit how you feel about neglecting your mission until now.

_____

_____

_____

_____

_____

_____

_____

_____

_____

_____

_____

_____

_____

3.07 *The Positive Past: There is no Loss*

Even if you have abandoned your mission on a conscious level, or passed over exciting chances to express it, your mission won't disappear. Who knows, maybe you were actually intended to express your mission fully at this very time. Perhaps this is the precise moment for an exciting rearrangement of your talents. Whether you're thirtysomething, fortysomething, fiftysomething or beyond, it's not too late to find your special niche in life. Although you have suffered some losses (we all do), the way you have lived your life is a part of the grand scheme of things. The sum of your past experience, including failures and successes, has moved you toward the present moment where only true opportunity awaits. Here is a chance to review and affirm your past.

1. What past experiences were fulfilling and positive?

_____

_____

_____

2. What did you learn during the time that you were not on target with your mission?

_____

_____

_____

3. How can you use your past experience to help you view the present more positively?

_____

_____

_____

4. Why is this exactly the right time to be working on your mission?

_____

_____

_____

3.08 *Letter Writing*

Other unacknowledged, harbored, or self-trivializing feelings can emerge through letter writing. Write a letter of apology to your mission, pay attention to any feelings of sadness, longing, pleasure, hope or self-defeat. These feelings may surface if you got off the track along the way, or if you missed an important career opportunity. Give yourself a chance to explore any emotions in this letter.

Dear Life Mission:

_____

_____

_____

_____

_____

_____

_____

_____

_____

_____

_____

_____

_____

_____

_____

_____

_____

3.09 *If the Shoe Fits . . .*

Write a letter to your mother, father, mate, friend, partner, teacher or any significant other. Thank them for their support in helping you to pursue your dream. Also, if the shoe fits, acknowledge anger or sadness if they discouraged you or failed to provide adequate support and encouragement. This letter of acknowledgement is written primarily for your own benefit, but if it is especially positive, you may wish to send or share it.

Dear _____

I want to acknowledge (give thanks, express anger, sadness) for

_____

_____

_____

_____

_____

_____

_____

_____

3.10 *Face Fear Daily*

Perhaps the most frequently cited emotional block impeding our forward progress is fear—fear of failure, fear of success, fear of monetary privation, fear of our family or friends' disapproval. Perhaps it is simply the universal fear of change or of the unknown. Review your list in exercise 3.01 for things that may be blocking the fulfillment of your dream. Write about these, or any other fears you might possibly be harboring.

I fear _____

_____

_____

_____

_____

_____

3.11 *Beyond the Comfort Zone*

Sometimes, by simply acknowledging our own fear, we dispel its power over our lives. We can feel the fear and proceed with our mission tasks anyway. At other times, our fear may be so intense that we don't know how to dispel it. For such intractable fear, embark on a daily program of emotional strengthening.

Identify five important activities that you tend to avoid. These may be simple tasks, such as making phone calls, shopping for clothes, or writing letters. They may also be more complicated, such as learning how to use a new computer program or taking a class.

Then rate these activities for their fear quotient. Use a scale from one one to five, five being the most scary activity, and one the least.

Activity	*Fear Quotient*
1. _____	_____
2. _____	_____
3. _____	_____
4. _____	_____
5. _____	_____

For the next week, practice some aspect of the least scary activity for at least 10 minutes every day. As you increase your emotional muscle strength, extend the time to 15 or 20 minutes, or move on to the next most scary task. Remember, the longer you harbor or feed a fear, the bigger it gets.

ACTION BLOCKS

The third area of blockage is in our actions or self-defeating behaviors. As the above exercise demonstrates, emotional or cognitive blocks result in inappropriate, inadequate or inconsistent action. Negative action patterns or habits are usually supported by underlying negative feelings or thoughts that need to be examined and worked through. Sometimes we can change our lives if we simply identify negative behavior patterns and begin to act differently.

Typical self-defeating behaviors are avoidance, poor time management, failure to prioritize, cluttering, procrastination, lack of scheduling or organization, inconsistent follow-through and fuzzy or scattered action plans. Some of these behaviors are explored in the FYSP book.

3.12 *Busting your Blocks*

A mission needs your go-ahead to become reality. Pick one block for examination. Have you taken all of the necessary steps to overcome your block? Have you tested it against reality?

Have you asked for help or information, and have you examined every alternative? Have you discussed this block with an expert or other appropriate person?

Let's say your block is, "I can't learn a foreign language." Have you taken language lessons? Do you know any foreign languages? Have you checked on various methods of language instruction to decide which method is best for you? Talked to people who are taking a foreign language class? Discussed your block in therapy? Practiced with a friend? Traveled in a foreign country?

Write down what you are blocked from doing and test it against the following checklist.

I am blocked from _____

_____

Checklist: Yes   No

In spite of being blocked, I do this activity often.   ☐   ☐
I am passionate about doing it.   ☐   ☐
I am capable of doing it.   ☐   ☐
I have learned how to do it.   ☐   ☐
My blocked activity is something no one can do.   ☐   ☐
I have researched this block.   ☐   ☐
I have spent a lot of time working on my block.   ☐   ☐
My block is based on experience.   ☐   ☐
Others have told me I can't do this.   ☐   ☐
I stand absolutely alone with my block.   ☐   ☐
I've discussed overcoming my block with an expert.   ☐   ☐

3.13 *I've done it before, I can do it again*

Pick out any resources which if used, would help you overcome your block (also consult your resource list from 1.13).

Example: My resources to overcome my writing block include the following:

- I got an A in a creative writing class.
- I won a prize in a high school writing contest.
- I had a letter published in our local paper.

My resources to overcome my blocks are:

_____

_____

_____

_____

_____

_____

If you ever did the thing from which you are blocked, why can't you do it again? What's different? What made it possible then? What action must you take in order to do it again? Do you need to take a class, get support, research the subject? Write about this here:

_____

_____

_____

_____

_____

_____

_____

_____

3.14 *Getting Clear*

Sometimes blocks result from too much clutter. Clearing things out is a sign of health and progress when you are working on your mission. The fewer brambles you have in your way, the better you can see the path. Eliminating the superfluous brings a lightness to life, an ability to appreciate your true gifts, a feeling of expansion and health. For fifteen minutes each day, examine what you can get rid of that's blocking your path. Work on tossing things out. (Remember, you can always give these things to others. Recycling is ecologically sound and a generous way to circulate your good to those who need it.)

Hint:

Reward yourself after each throw away session. Continue to work down the list until you have completed all the items.

Cluttered areas that need clearing

- ☐ closets
- ☐ files
- ☐ address books and cards
- ☐ diversions
- ☐ ideas I don't intend to follow through on
- ☐ car
- ☐ garage
- ☐ friends
- ☐ family members
- ☐ household goods
- ☐ storage space
- ☐ books
- ☐ office
- ☐ kitchen
- ☐ unnecessary duplicates (radios, tvs, computers, appliances)
- ☐ other (list):

Prioritize and pick your top three choices for elimination.

1. _____
2. _____
3. _____

List three ways that you can eliminate your first item.

1. _____
2. _____
3. _____

3.15 *Dissolving, Resolving, and Transforming Blocks*

Let's experiment with a creative visualization exercise to resolve emotional blocks. To begin, find a quiet place where you can relax and do some deep breathing. Now, close your eyes and imagine yourself walking down a path. Notice the scenery to your right and left, feel the texture of the path. As you come to a fork in the road, choose which road you will take. Ahead of you lies an obstacle of some sort—this can be a person, an animal, or any object that gets in your way. Notice the shape, color, size and texture of this barrier.

In the space below, use colored pencils or crayons to draw a picture of your block.

Now, find an imaginative way to get around this obstacle or transform your block into some manageable form so that you can continue on your way. What obstacle did you see, and how did you overcome or transform it? What did you learn about the nature of your emotional block?

_____

_____

_____

_____

_____

_____

3.16 *Organization: A Major Key to Block-Busting*

Pick a typical work week to log your activities. Make an entry for each hour from 8 A.M. to 8 P.M.
Check your activities against the following questions:

a) What repetitive actions can be combined, reduced, or even eliminated (i.e. photocopying, telephoning, trips to the bank, visits to grocery stores)?

_____

_____

_____

b) Which tasks directly relate to your goals and mission? (refer to exercise 2.08)

_____

_____

_____

c) Which activities went smoothly? Which ones were most challenging? Which ones did you resist?

_____

_____

_____

d) Examine how you might better deal with the tasks you resisted. Can you delegate them or change how you look at them? For instance, can you see paying bills not as a duty, but rather as circulating your good back into the universe?

_____

_____

_____

e) Do you adjust your activities to your energy cycle? Do you do important work at your high energy times?

_____

_____

_____

How do you revive yourself at low times: sports, walks, naps, fun things, low priority tasks, meeting friends for coffee?

_____

_____

_____

f) On a scale of 1-10 (10 being "very satisfied" and 1 being "very dissatisfied") rate yourself on what you wanted to accomplish this particular day against what you actually completed.

1___2___3___4___5___6___7___8___9___10____

g) What can you do to improve the rating you gave yourself?

_____

_____

_____

_____

In order to review your organizational progress, this exercise can be repeated at given intervals—(i.e. on certain days of a selected week, once a week, once a month).

Here are some further guidelines for organization:

1. Do only one thing at a time.
2. Reward yourself when you break a self-defeating pattern.
3. Work in chunks of time: continue if it works, stop when it doesn't.
4. Take breaks!
5. Complete one thing before going on to the next.
6. Call someone when you're stuck, and ask for help.
7. Visualize the result you want before you begin.
8. Know when it's better to work with someone, and know when you need to do it alone.
9. Your additional suggestions:

_____

_____

_____

Module Three Review Questions

1. Which of the three blocks occurs most often in my life? When?

_____

_____

_____

2. What idea killers do I use most often? In what context?

_____

_____

_____

3. What do my blocks reveal about what I love to do?

_____

_____

_____

4. What methods have I used to overcome blocks in the past?

_____

_____

_____

5. How do my self-fulfilling prophecies get in the way of manifesting my mission?

_____

_____

_____

6. What "payoffs" do my blocks give me? What benefits do I imagine getting from not pursuing my mission?

_____

_____

_____

7. What have I gained from the path I have chosen up to now?

_____

_____

8. How has my path contributed to where I am now?

_____

_____

_____

9. What do I stand to gain by changing my path now?

_____

_____

_____

10. What can I do today to eliminate just one block?

_____

_____

_____

11. Which clutter needs to leave my life, and how will I remove it?

_____

_____

_____

12. What did I learn about the nature and appearance of my block?

_____

_____

_____

13. How can I dissolve this kind of block?

_____

_____

_____

MODULE FOUR:
Your Personal Mode

(Strongly recommended reading: Chapter 2, FYSP)

You may do things with a splash or with a dash. You may hash them over, or you may do them without flash. Any way that you name it, it's your individual personal mode of operation, akin to your own DNA. Once we have identified a dream and the barriers which block us, it helps to take a closer look at our own style of doing things to understand our process.

Each of us has a clear preference for doing things in a particular way. We call this preference your personal mode of operation, or PM. Your PM reflects the how, or the way you want to accomplish your mission.

In Module Four, you will learn about your PM and its characteristics. You'll learn how to identify your chief PM and how this knowledge can help you achieve your Life Mission more easily.

4.01 *Caveat Emptor (Buyer Beware!)*

Think of your most important purchase, (TV, VCR, couch, car, house) and check your preference for the procedure that you used in making the transaction.

A) Did you . . .

_____1) buy it immediately without much thought

_____2) get it for its appeal to your senses

_____3) secure it for sturdiness and durability

_____4) purchase it only after exhaustive research and investigation

B) Were you motivated by . . .

_____1) getting it now

_____2) tickling your fancy

_____3) the need for stability

_____4) making the right decision

C) Was your process speed . . .

_____1) fast and firm

_____2) flashy and with feeling

_____3) measured and moderate

_____4) slow and selective

D) Are you driven by the need for . . .

_____1) results

_____2) approval

_____3) security

_____4) quality

Each number above represents a distinct category, or PM. You probably checked the same number from each section at least two, if not three or even four times. Let's move to a larger inventory now to see what these categories mean.

4.02 *Getting Conscious of your Personal Mode (PM)*

Your PM and mission go hand in hand.

Knowing your PM is important, because a mission must combine what you want and how you want it to be achieved. You can validate and appreciate your PM when you understand it. If you misuse your PM through lack of knowledge, it can lead to feelings of low self-worth, inadequacy, depression or frustration. Ignorance is not bliss!

Your effectiveness depends on a PM that is comfortable, easy, and suitable to you. Go with your PM, and your mission process will flow naturally and beautifully. Then, you are not paddling upstream; you are rowing your boat gently down *your* stream.

Each PM describes a particular way you like to act to get the results you want. It represents a preference, not a skill. Your PM is valid for doing things the way YOU want them done.

Continue determining which mode you prefer with this simple, in-depth inventory.

Working horizontally, rate each of the four words for how it describes your behavior. Use all four numbers for each row.

4 = describes me most   3 = next highest   2 = next to lowest,   1 = lowest.

Sample Answer:

3 strong-willed   4 enthusiastic   2 responsive   1 organized

__ strong-willed
__ decisive
__ competitive
__ self-assured
__ makes waves
__ pragmatic
__ blunt
__ tough
__ impatient
__ dominating
__ cold
__ action-oriented
__ self starter
__ accepts challenge
__ likes risks
__ forceful opinions
__ quick
__ works on hunches
__ seeks challenges
__ likes conflict

__ enthusiastic
__ influential
__ gullible
__ humorous
__ imaginative
__ charming
__ emotional
__ self-promoting
__ impulsive
__ manipulative
__ dramatic
__ idea person
__ high contact person
__ uses intuition
__ likes persuasion
__ likes fun jobs
__ likes to motivate
__ disorganized
__ visionary
__ likes harmony

Total_____

_____

Inventory

__ responsive
__ agreeable
__ calm
__ supportive
__ dependable
__ territorial
__ low key
__ team player
__ predictable
__ loyal
__ thorough
__ good listener
__ systematic
__ sticks to procedure
__ likes small groups
__ likes structure
__ quiet in meetings
__ methodical
__ traditional
__ likes security

____

__ organized
__ orderly
__ non-demonstrative
__ indecisive
__ exacting
__ conscientious
__ restrained
__ critical
__ disciplined
__ meticulous
__ proper
__ evaluates
__ works alone
__ slow-paced
__ non-verbal
__ business-like
__ respects facts
__ problem solver
__ likes clarity
__ likes perfection

____

Scoring Key

Add up the totals for each column. Give yourself an additional point for each of the four numbers you selected in 4.01 and add these to your total.

_____   _____   _____   _____

A high in column 1 = Doer, 2 = Motivator, 3 = Stabilizer, 4 = Analyzer

My highest total is _____ I am a _____

My second highest total is _____ I am a _____

As you can see, there are basic differences between the four categories. In brief, beyond the obvious preferences their names suggest, Doers desire results, make quick decisions based on little information, and they must be #1. Motivators like approval, ideas, and visions. Stabilizers prefer follow-through, consistency, and security, while Analyzers honor connectedness, information, and accuracy. (For more details, read FYSP, Chapter Two, "Mission a la Mode".)

Based on what you now know about PMs, guess what category the following people probably belong to:

Saddam Hussein _____
Albert Einstein _____
Mother Theresa _____
Lily Tomlin _____

List four people in your life who show a clear preference for one PM (draw from co-workers, friends, famous people or family.).

Doer _____
Motivator _____
Stabilizer _____
Analyzer _____

4.03 *My Personal Mode (PM) Summary:*

1. My dominant strength is _____

_____

_____

2. I can use my PM in the mission search to help _____

_____

_____

_____

3. Non PM strengths I can draw upon are_____

_____

_____

_____

4. My most underdeveloped strength is _____

_____

_____

5. The effect of using my underdeveloped strength often results in

_____

_____

_____

_____

6. I tend to overuse my dominant strength when I _____

_____

_____

_____

_____

Fieldwork:

You will need time to observe your PM in order to get comfortable using it effectively. Pay attention to how your PM manifests in your personal and professional life, and which behaviors do or do not work for you. Watch how you use some of the characteristics in the list above. Then, observe others and practice identifying their characteristics.

4.04 *Going my Way?*

List at least five ways of doing things that are most characteristic of your PM.

Example: I like to dream up ideas.
(P.S. Can you guess which PM this style represents?)

_____

_____

_____

_____

_____

How can you apply these ways of doing things more effectively so that your mission search will be more enriching?

_____

_____

_____

_____

_____

_____

_____

_____

4.05 *Low Blows*

We sometimes behave in ways that are incompatible with our PM. For example, let's say that you prefer to proceed in a low-key, careful, meticulous manner (without flash). But, you feel pressured by parents, friends, mates or society to perform in an award-winning fashion. Buying into that model, you race down the fast track of achievement, earning awards or degrees. Sooner or later, you'll begin feeling stressed out. You may experience physical problems ("If I go against my grain, I'll get a migraine"). Or you may just feel unhappy. You may conclude that you are a failure at your work, although the truth is your PM makes you unsuited for that particular kind of work.

Go back over the list in exercise 4.02, and identify at least five behaviors which definitely do not suit you. They may be strengths to OTHERS, but not to you. Do not judge them, just choose those traits you don't care to use.

_____

_____

_____

_____

_____

In what situations do you find yourself using these traits?

_____

_____

Do you use any of these traits just because you think you should? Why?

_____

_____

_____

What traits could you use in their place?

_____

_____

4.06 *Caution: Low Preferences at Work!*

A conscious examination of low preferences can offer insight into problems that you may be having in the Life Mission process. For example, if you are a person with a Doer PM, you may not incubate ideas because you prefer to make snap decisions. Nevertheless, some steps in the mission process require time and patience. Pausing to look before you leap can prove to be a valuable exercise. If you learn to identify, manage and work on your low preferences, you can improve your success with the mission search.

Look at the list of words in your lowest preference column, exercise 4.02. Use one low preference word for each statement, and fill in the blanks below.

1. I tend to underuse my preference of _____

2. When I am anxious, I tend to avoid _____

3. I tend to neglect using my trait of _____
in the following situation:

_____

_____

4. I dislike using _____ especially when I

_____

_____

5. I get into trouble using _____, particularly
when I_____

_____

_____

6. I am most uncomfortable when I use my low PM of _____

_____

because _____

_____

Fieldwork:

Pick a low preference and recall a situation in which you tend to avoid using it. For example: the low preference "meticulous" might correspond with the situation "I avoid reading labels when I shop."

Make an action plan for using your low PM to get positive results. Be specific.

Example: "I will read the label of at least one cleaning product at a supermarket today. I will focus on whether it is tested on animals, and if it has any chemicals harmful to me and the environment." Then carry out your plan until you feel comfortable with that low PM trait.

4.07 *Your Dream and your PM*

Let's let your low PM assist your high PM in manifesting your dream. This exercise has five steps.

1) Write your dream from page 38 here.

_____

_____

2) What is an obstacle to that dream?

_____

_____

3) What is your PM, and how can it help you overcome obstacles to your dream?

_____

4) How can your work on a low preference PM help you overcome obstacles to your dream?

_____

_____

5) Write out an action plan using the above information.

__ _____

__ _____

__ _____

Example:
1) My dream is to go to the next Olympics.
2) My obstacle is that I don't have enough money saved.
3) My PM is Analyzer; I love details and doing research; this can help me investigate ways to save money, and where to get the the cheapest flights.
4) My low preference PM word is "taking risks". By working on this low preference I can gain confidence to travel alone for a week to the Olympics.
5) My action plan is to reread "Risk Daily" in FYSP. I will work on my low preference PM by taking a short trip without having every detail worked out in advance.

Module Four Review Questions

1. What are the chief characteristics of my PM?

_____

_____

_____

2. List the chief characteristics of the other three PM's.

_____

_____

_____

3. How does my PM relate to my mission?

_____

_____

_____

4. What are my low preferences? Do I con myself by thinking I must use them? How?

_____

_____

_____

5. How can I use my chief PM to further my mission?

_____

_____

_____

6. How can I use a low preference PM to enhance my mission search?

_____

_____

_____

7. How can I overcome blocks to my dream by using my high and low PM?

_____

_____

_____

MODULE FIVE:
Gathering Clues

(Strongly recommended reading: Chapter 3, 4 and 9 in the FYSP)

In this module, the goal is to sharpen your ability to generate clues easily and quickly. In Modules One through Four, we concentrated on process exercises from which you learned to derive clues. Now, we'll focus on exercises specifically designed to trigger immediate clues to your mission. These exercises will embellish and expand on your work in the first four modules.

Seeking clues is a daily activity; nothing should be overlooked. Even the smallest piece of information can provide new revelations for your mission search.

You are your own archaeological site. The treasures—all of your precious findings—are within you. All you need is to explore, persevere, and be ever vigilant for clues and their meaning to you.

After completing this module, you will be able to do the following:

1) Generate clues easily and quickly.
2) Gather more clues for insight into your mission.
3) Gain greater clarity on your mission.

In this module, we will give you numerous ways to trigger these clues. Transfer them to the Clue Section. Enjoy!

5.01 *"ing" Go the Strings of my Heart*

The greatest clue to your mission comes from the heart. What do you enjoy doing? For consistency, use "ing" forms (reading, cooking, traveling, acting) and make sure that you observe the following guidelines:

1) You actually like the activities you list.
2) You have done them or experienced them before.
3) You list only one "ing" activity per example.
4) You are specific.

The end result should look something like this: "I enjoy riding my 12-speed bike along the Susquehanna River in the Springtime."

Carry a small pocket notebook to record any experience that triggers a rumble in you; it's like a seismograph indicating a tremor. We call it "catching yourself in the act of enjoying something." When you have such an experience, write down one word that best describes your enjoyment.

For example, let's say that on your way home from work you hear a song that you like on the car radio. Write down a cue word: music. Now, incorporate it into a sentence beginning with "I enjoy." Ex: I enjoy listening to music.

Then, ask any additional questions of yourself to narrow down your enjoyment:

1. What kind of music do I enjoy listening to?
   I enjoy listening to *popular music.*

More specifically:

2. What kind of popular music?
   I enjoy listening to popular music performed by *female vocalists.*

More specifically:

3. Which female vocalist do I most enjoy listening to?
   I enjoy listening to popular music performed by *Doris Day.*

More specifically:

4. Which music by Doris Day do I most enjoy listening to?
   I enjoy listening to the song *Move Over, Darling* performed by
   Doris Day.

My final "ing" statement is:

> *I enjoy listening to the song Move Over, Darling performed by*
> *Doris Day.*

This is an exercise in clarity of choice. Your final "ings" do not
mean that you may never listen to a male vocalist, or other songs by
Doris Day, or classical music, or instrumental music. It simply
means you have identified listening to a particular song by a particular artist as a specific activity that you enjoy.

Caution: this is a process. Your results will be better if you don't
try to do the entire "ing" sequence at once, but rather in small chunks.
Be sure that each example represents something you actually enjoy
doing or something you have done—even if you haven't done it for
a while. Remember to be concise!

If you have difficulty finding example of favorite "ings," here are
some helpful hints to trigger material for this exercise. As you go
about your daily routine, identify activities you enjoy most by ask-
ing yourself these questions:

What do I focus on while I'm driving, shopping, walking,
   traveling ?
What do I pay attention to when people chat?
What section do I read first in the paper?
What subjects cause me to perk up in a conversation?
What movies or songs do I prefer?
What radio and TV programs do I listen to regularly?
What kinds of events interest me?
What subjects do I talk about often with great enthusiasm?
What haven't I allowed myself to do in my free time that's fun?

Now, it's your turn. When you've identified an enjoyment, turn
it into a sentence. Is it specific (like our example)? If not, continue
until your final "ing" sentence is so clear and focused that *ten* people

would all say the same thing if you asked them to interpret it. In other words, If you have to explain the sentences to anyone, your "ing" still lacks specificity. For now, just work on ONE example.

I enjoy

_____

_____

_____

Fieldwork:

Identify five or six enjoyments, and see what they have in common. Transfer to Clue Section.

5.02 *On the "Go-Get": Environment Triggers*

When do you get your ideas? After a walk, while you are sleeping, after a workout or meditation? Note what triggers your creative thinking and what ideas it sparks.

Example:

Trigger:	*What this sparks:*
Taking a walk	Workshop exercises

Trigger:	*What This Sparks:*
___ _____	_____
_____	_____
_____	_____
_____	_____
_____	_____
_____	_____
_____	_____

5.03 *Get Thee to a Library*

Go to a library or bookstore with a good magazine section. See which publications attract your attention. Be careful not to read anything too thoroughly—just browse quickly. Pick ONE magazine and scan the articles. Which ones interests you most? Is it funny? Informative? Does it concern a famous person? Feature a new invention? Discuss a creative career change? Describe a successful business? Write the article title.

List four articles you were most interested in:

_____

I liked articles about _____
_____
_____
_____

and especially one about _____
_____
_____

because _____
_____
_____
_____
_____

Extract from your answers the very essence of your interest, and transfer it to your clue section.

Fieldwork:

You can expand this exercise to include several publications. Look for what the articles you pick have in common, "the clue behind the clue." For instance, let's say that you like people who have achieved something against all odds. What kind of achievement was it? What sort of people were involved? What did you like best about the achievement? Two people interested in the same article or subject may have very different reasons for that interest! Your particular point of interest provides further clues. You might focus on bicycling around the world. Another person might like helping the handicapped. Still another might be attracted to unusual sporting events.

5.04 *Jealousy, Night and Day You Torture Me . . .*

What arouses your jealousy or envy? What makes you ask, "I could be doing that! "Why didn't they ask me to do that?" Before you dismiss jealousy as one of the seven deadly sins, consider that it can tell you a lot about your mission. Why? Because your jealousy shows something that you could be doing—now!

I am jealous of _____

_____

_____

To stimulate your envy, watch for people or events that attract your attention. Look at articles in the newspaper, coming attractions in your city, items in the news, people's comments. Jot down ideas.

Example: An author comes to town to discuss her best-selling book about tree frogs. You notice you are jealous. Is it the author's field of study that makes you jealous? Is it that she has written a book? Or has she won an award for writing a best-seller that arouses your envy and admiration? Or is the woman is a fantastic speaker? Is she paid well for her work? Is she the first minority to earn this award?

In the following week, notice your jealousies and what they specifically relate to. Put them in your note book. Then pick one example, and analyze precisely what you are jealous about as a means to uncover what we call the "clue within a clue."

I am jealous of _____

_____

_____

The part which makes me jealous is _____

_____

_____

This feeling of jealousy tells me I need to _____

_____

_____

Transfer your insights to your Clue Section.

5.05 *Quickies*

And now for some quick ways to gather more clues. Do these exercises rapidly. They are not meant for long obsessing. Spend no more than a minute or so doing each one. (Doers and Motivators will like this; Analyzers and Stabilizers will be less comfortable with this approach.)

You can expand on any of these exercises later. We'll give you some fieldwork suggestions which can also be done at your leisure. For now, do only what is asked here and go on to the next quickie until you wish to stop. Remember, less is more!

a) Timelessness

List one activity in which you get so absorbed that you forget the time.

_____

_____

b) Energy

What gives you energy? Imagine that you come home tired and fatigued, too tired even to make yourself supper. As you drag yourself through the door, you get a phone call from a friend inviting you to do something. You are instantly energized and ready to go! What were you invited to do?

_____

_____

c) Fun!

What do you do for fun? Guess what? A mission is supposed to be fun. It's important to mix in that ingredient as well.

List one thing you do for fun:

_____

_____

d) S/Heroes

Heroes can be culled from historical figures, mythology, fairy tales, children's books, Bible stories, movies, parables, current events, history books, fantasy, people from operas and musicals, people you know by reputation and people you know personally.

Fieldwork:

Remember the things you did as a child—skipping stones, ice skating, taking walks with your pooch, swimming, riding your bike or taking off with the family for vacation.

Write down several things you did or still do for fun.

What do they have in common?

Transfer to the Clue Section.

91

Who is your greatest hero (or shero)? What attribute about her/him do you admire?

My S/hero is: _____

_____

Fieldwork:

Make a list of your s/heroes, their traits, and write down what they have in common.

Traits I like about this person are:

_____

e) Childhood Games

What games or activities did you play as a child? List a favorite one here.

_____

_____

Fieldwork:

Write down several games or activities you engaged in as a child. Did you play by yourself? Did you organize others to play with you? Were you a follower? Were the games solitary or group? Did you like being outdoors? Were you active or contemplative? Were the games competitive? Did they involve development of a skill? Can you think of any other descriptions of your activities?

f) " . . . these are a few of of my favorite things . . ."

As a child, was there something you liked doing repeatedly? Did you like reading the same book 10-15 times, going to the same movie over and over, collecting things, or playing the same game? Or did you beg your parents to take you somewhere, or ask to do something again and again? List one favorite thing :

_____

g) Career Fantasies

What career fantasies do you have now? Name three: one which you could do without further training, another which you could do with some additional training, and another that you could learn but you haven't the foggiest notion how. Remember, this is a fantasy. Use creative titles, such as Empress of the Universe, L.A. Swat Team Member, The Blue Fairy or Wizard; it will add flavor to the thing you want to do.

Career Fantasy #1:(no further training)

_____

_____

Career Fantasy #2: (some further training)

_____

_____

Career Fantasy #3: (requires a lot of training)

_____

_____

h) You Can Have It All

You're attending a very unusual school. The only requirements are: you enjoy every class you take, you feel enthusiastic about the subject, you really like the material. List one favorite course that you would take. Do not pay attention to whether you have time, money, or background for it. Simply focus on something you are passionate about.

j) Hollywood! Dadadadadadada Hollywood . . .

Select your favorite movie. What attracted your interest (Like the actors, plot, setting or most important scene).

_____

_____

k) Somewhere There's Music

Do the same for a favorite song. What moves you about this song (i.e. mood, lyrics, message, melody)?

_____

_____

l) Mission Possible

The original TV program *Mission Impossible* featured Jim Phelps, an agent whose assignment (called a Mission) was delivered to him each week on a tape. Imagine that your mission is being delivered to you on tape. What might be on it? Be spontaneous and creative. Go for an assignment you would enjoy. Be specific!

Mission Assignment:

_____

_____

Now go back over the exercises and transfer any insights into your Clue Section. Do the fieldwork exercises at your leisure and put them into your notebook. Then transfer information to your Clue Section.

Fieldwork:

Get ideas by looking at college catalogs, extension programs, adult schools, and seminar brochures. Invent your own titles! Write the titles or subject description that interests you into your notebook and transfer anything they have in common to your Clue Section.

Fieldwork:

Copy down lyrics from favorite songs and derive clues about yourself from them. If you don't know the lyrics, go to a music store or library to hunt them up.

Module Five Review Questions:

1. How do my clues from this Module relate to Modules 1-4?

_____

_____

_____

_____

_____

2. What specific insight did I get from the "ing" exercise?

_____

_____

_____

_____

_____

3. What do my "ing" statements have in common?

_____

_____

_____

_____

_____

4. What clues did I derive from the quickies?

_____

_____

_____

_____

_____

5. Do any of these quickie items have anything in common?

_____

_____

_____

_____

_____

6. What is my "mission possible"?

_____

_____

_____

_____

_____

7. How does my mission tape relate to my clues?

_____

_____

_____

_____

_____

8. Are there any clues which stand out in this module? Which ones,
   and why?

_____

_____

_____

_____

_____

MODULE SIX:
Synthesis: Writing Your Personal Mission Statement

If you have completed the previous exercises in this book, you have developed a wealth of information in the form of clues about your mission. In their totality, clues represent the ingredients of your mission. Now it is time to synthesize your clues to "face the music" and hear the theme of your life.

6.01 *String of Pearls*

You are embarking on the last major step of your mission search. You'll now be creating what we call a "String of Pearls." A string of pearls is a synthesis of the clues you have gathered during the last five modules. Each pearl represents one area of interest or passion; when strung together, they form the sum total of your mission. Once you see the pearls in a circle, you'll begin to make connections between them. It may take some time, but it will happen. In the middle of the string we have the *sine qua non*—that one thing that relates to all the others and to which all others point: your mission.

Let's take a look at the string of pearls on p. 101, the example of Jacques Cousteau. We've identified only the most obvious of his pearls (can you add some of your own?). Each of the pearls relates to the others in some significant way. For example, a book Cousteau wrote (pearl: writing), had to do with sharks (pearl: marine life). Each of these pearls in turn relates to the center of the pearls: the ocean.

In this module, you will work to define your cluster areas of interest, or pearls, and then find the essence of all these pearls, which is your mission.

Let's take a look at the string of pearls on p. 101, the example of

Your task now is to do the following:
1) Organize your clues into pearls
2) Name each pearl
3) Identify the essential core word for your mission.

Here's the sequence:
Clues > putting into categories > naming the pearl > finding the *sine qua non*

Spend as much time as you need on this section. Follow the format below carefully and completely. Your overall goal is to find commonalities among your clues.

Example:

macadamia nut ice cream	> ice cream / macadamia nuts
travel to tropical islands	> tropics / islands / travel

First, put all of your clues from Modules 1-5 together on a large sheet (preferably a flip chart) on small post-its. Second, look for the same clues which occur repeatedly, such as subjects that deal with

Fieldwork:

Each of your clues should contain a central word or concept. If any clue contains several words, you may want to divide it into several categories for further clarity.

sports, travel or music. Put those post-its together onto separate areas of the flip chart or onto separate sheets if necessary.

Third, organize similar clues together. This will require some thought on your part. Remember what we said about the clue within a clue. You'll have to decide just what the similarity is amongst these items. For example, if you have clues such as "fruit," "apple pie," and "ice cream," you could cluster them as "sweets," "cooking," or even "nutrition." Sometimes looking over your clues will help you pinpoint that one description which binds all your similar clues together. Using post-its will enable you to change them around. You might decide that one belongs to a different category than you had originally thought.

Fourth, take those single post-its, or ones that just don't seem to fit and put them all together. Sometimes you'll recognize a commonality between them that you hadn't even suspected!

Now, looking over your various categories of post-its, think of a word which describes each category, and transfer it into the space provided on the string of pearls page. Work with pencil, or make a photocopy of the page so you can make revisions later.

Label as many pearls as you need (a string of pearls is not the same length for everyone). Caution: Avoid using professions or job categories.

"pearls" from clients have included:

brass instruments	outdoors
things Italian	trains
paper	party games
trees	ancient sites
puzzles	mountains
folk music	rivers

Just for now, put a word in the top part of the circle on the middle of the page. It should connect to, capture, and summarize all the pearls. It is your *sine qua non*, your abiding love. If you are not sure of one word, put one in anyway just to see how it feels. Try different words until you're satisfied that the center fits, just like the last piece of a puzzle. It may take time, so be patient. You can always make changes as you go along.

6.02 *Writing Your Personal Mission Statement*

Now you'll create your mission statement. The goal is not to define a career, but to create an umbrella concept of who you are and what your essence is. When your mission statement comes from that place of deep focused desire, you should be able to relate it to any level of your life: career, avocation, recreation, hobby, personal time, education, training, spiritual development or physical expression.

Mission statements are challenging and require much thought. You may rewrite your statement several times over the course of reflection. Your mission is a blueprint for your life as you see it now. Give yourself the option to refine, edit, and change it until you have formulated it to your satisfaction.

An effective way to construct a mission statement is to begin with the word in the middle of the string of pearls. You are here to express this essence in a particular way. It is your abiding love, reflecting your talents and interests, and it connects to your pearls.

Here is an example of a short mission statement which Cousteau might have written:

Ocean: With my abiding love of the ocean, I am here to inform the planet on how to keep that ocean safe, by means of my research, film-making and diving. I am Poseidon/Neptune, Protector of the Seas.

Here is Naomi Stephan's mission statement:

Sound: With my abiding love of music, I am here to create a sound world by means of the sound of my choral compositions and words for Life Mission seekers who want to hear it. I am a Wizard of Ah's.

Think about how you wish to use the core part of you. What do you plan to give, or by what means do you intend to carry out your gift, and, if relevant, to whom? What does this essence mean to you? In what ways can you use it to serve self and others? This statement should apply, in some way, to any situation you are in. (For instance, when Cousteau is traveling, it is in connection with the ocean, i.e., to visit another ocean site, to research, to relax and recuperate at the seaside, or to just have fun diving.) Remember, connection is the key. All things connect to the mission, and YOU connect to your mission.

Fieldwork:

If you get stuck, think of an abiding love—something you could not do without. Without it, your world would look very bleak indeed. (Ex: having access to the ocean is indispensable for Cousteau, as was the ability to hear music for Beethoven.)

String of Pearls

(Jacques Cousteau)

Film-making

Physiology

Photography

Travel

Ecology

Mission:
The Ocean

Mission Statement:

Ocean: With my abiding love of the ocean, I am here to inform the planet on how to keep that ocean safe, by means of my research, film-making and diving. I am Poseidon/Neptune, Protector of the Seas.

Invention

Adventure

Writing

Flying

Biology

Ships

Marine Life

Now fill in the blanks to construct a beginning mission statement:

With my abiding love of _____ I am here to _____

_____

(what I want to create with my mission), which I will accomplish by means of _____

(my talents and gifts) for the greater good of _____

(whom I wish to give to) _____ A metaphor for me is _____

_____

Fieldwork:

Read mission statements of organizations and businesses. Are they specific? Do they have a definable purpose? How do they express their purpose?

Put this mission statement below the line in the center circle of the string of pearls. Leave it there to examine for several days, or even weeks. Every time you see it, check it out for its relevance, its accuracy, its specificity for your life now. Make any changes and revisions which you feel are necessary. When you are satisfied you don't need to make any further changes, you'll have your mission statement in place. With your mission in mind, you'll be ready to put it into action, which is the subject of Module Seven.

Find out if anyone has done something similar to your mission. Interview someone about their mission. Read about people's missions as revealed in biographies, magazines and newspapers. Note how they expressed their missions and the path that led to them.

Module Six Review Questions

1 Have I put the clues into single words or short phrases?

_____

_____

2. What sameness or similarities did I find for these clues?

_____

_____

3. What did I learn from the isolated clues I could not categorize?

_____

_____

Your String of Pearls

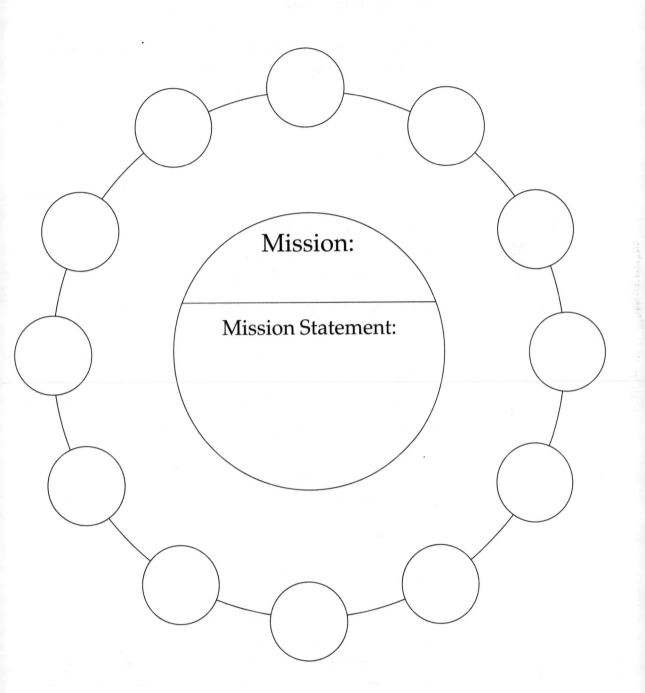

Mission:

Mission Statement:

3. What pearls did I identify based on the cluster of interest?

_____

_____

4. What one word did I derive from all these pearls which represents my abiding love, the core of my mission?

_____

5. On what gifts, talents and passions do I base my mission?

_____

_____

_____

6. To whom is my mission directed?

_____

_____

7. Am I clear about the means with which I intend to accomplish this mission? If so, how will I do this?

_____

_____

_____

8. Have I characterized my mission as a metaphor or in some colorful, non-literal way? What is it?

_____

_____

9. What is the result that I want from this mission?

_____

_____

10. How is my mission going to benefit others?

_____

_____

_____

MODULE SEVEN:
Manifesting Your Mission

Congratulations! You have identified your mission with its central core and many parts, or pearls. So much is open to you now that you have empowered yourself with a clear and powerful mission statement. This is a critical juncture in the mission process. You'll no doubt feel energized, but perhaps a bit scared as well. What do I do now?, you might ask. The first step is to decide on which part of your mission you wish to concentrate. (Remember, you can have it all, just not all at once.)

Module Seven will furnish you with the tools to translate your mission into specific action by breaking it down into a manageable part, which we will call a project, with which you can energize and express your mission.

Do you want to write? Volunteer with the Peace Corps? Downsize your life to spend more time with your family? Teach computer literacy on a reservation? We call this process of identification, selecting a part, and working on a project "Giving Your Mission Muscle."

As you can see, your choice can take the form of work, an avocation, a hobby, a sabbatical—or even a vacation! For now, the important thing is to move forward. There is a section at the end of the module to record ideas.

After finishing this Module you should be able to do the following:

1) Cite ways to prepare for, and energize your mission.
2) Generate ideas for projects to launch your mission.
3) Isolate one project to begin with.
4) Stay on target even when difficulties arise.

Before selecting your project, here are some preparatory exercises which will give you ideas, encouragement and structure to complete the final stage of this workbook.

7.01 *Oh Mission! Rekindling a Lost Love*

Fieldwork:

Keep in mind that you are simply experimenting with ways to rekindle your passions. Keep a written commentary about your reactions. Did you resist doing the exercises? What emotions surfaced? Were your feelings predictable or did they surprise you? What does your choice tell you about yourself and your mission?

Chances are that what you are consistently avoiding is an important starting point for a project. Omission can be a helpful manifestation clue (although we are not recommending omission as a device to help you find clues!). Look at your pearls. Is there anything you love to do related to a pearl that you have avoided for a while? Or is there perhaps a project that you have worked on only sporadically? In other words, are there any loves within those pearls that you have omitted from your life?

Renew contact with an old love by devoting time each day to it. Anytime your energize a pearl or part of a pearl, you will energize your mission. Do you have a pearl named music? Maybe your piano is gathering dust. Play it! Is a pearl perhaps the outdoors? Have you neglected your passion of hiking in the woods or going for a walk? Maybe a pearl is "interiors". Or have you a piece of furniture you haven't refinished? Refinish it! Do not pay attention to results, for now. Just shower this lost passion with a lot of love.

Monitor your reactions as you go. Did you respond to this love in ways you hadn't anticipated? Notice whether or not you enjoyed yourself, whether any guilt, anxiety or unexpected feelings surfaced. Is your love still so attractive as before? Of course, it's okay to spend more than a few minutes a day, if you wish (chances are, you'll like it!). How could you revive this lost love? Are there any other lost loves within your pearls that you could renew contact with later?

Write about this rekindling process here:

I reconnect with my lost love of _____

_____

_____

_____

_____

_____

_____

7.02 *Basic Training: Breaking the Rules*

Manifesting a mission means that you will be taking risks, maybe even bending some rules. Do you have qualms about that? All rules are agreed-upon guidelines. Over time they get rewritten (i.e., broken) again and again.

Rules fall into two categories: societal and personal. Societal rules are commonly called laws. Most of us agree to abide by these laws. But if you were rushing a sick child to a hospital late at night down a lonely stretch of highway, would you exceed the speed limit? Given those circumstances you might decide to break a rule—even if it is wrong.

NOTE: Breaking rules must occur from your desire for the greater good of all concerned. We are NOT advocating that you break the law. Rather, we want you to identify those "rules" which have kept you from expressing your mission. Please remember, when it comes to rules, you must: 1) not contradict your principles, 2) stay within your financial means, 3) not endanger your life or the lives of others , 4) accept responsibility for your actions.

It cannot be denied, however, that there are societal rules which need to be changed because they hinder us from manifesting our mission. Some folks break their unspoken societal rules with great courage. An example is Alberta Hunter, the famous jazz singer. After taking time out to become a nurse, Alberta returned to the stage at age 80 and performed until shortly before her death at age 89. She simply refused to follow any rules about age and female singers! Or Rosa Parks, who refused to sit in the back of the bus.

Other examples of societal rules from our clients are:

Societal:
"Women can't do the work of longshoremen."
"Men shouldn't take time out from their careers."

List two societal rules that you believe are outdated or outmoded and that you need to break:

Societal Rules:

_____

_____

Explain how these rules have blocked you on your mission path:

_____

_____

_____

_____

Fieldwork:

Look for articles on societal and personal rules which have been broken for the greater good. A good starting point is in history. Societal rules stated that Rosa Parks must not sit in the front of the bus. She broke that "rule." When you find one, jot it down in your project section at the end of this module.

Analyze how you could change the rules to unblock your progress towards your mission:

_____

_____

_____

_____

_____

_____

Even though we might not incur any fines or punishment for breaking personal rules, they have their own particular grip on us anyway. Personal rules are hard to break and we find ourselves sticking to them even if they no longer match our beliefs or desires. An example of a worn-out rule might be: "Stick to your own" or having nothing to do with people outside your ethnic group.

Personal:
"I starve if I quit my job to become a writer."
"I can't run for office if I'm gay."

7:03 *Getting Results*

Now write down one of your personal rules, particularly one which is keeping you from a goal you would like to reach. State the goal that you would attain if you could just break your rule. Then, re-write the rule, and state what result you will gain from "breaking" it.

Example:

My rule: "I can't attend college if I have kids."
My unmet goal: "To attend college"
My rule breaker: "I can leave the kids in an after-school
                      program and take a day class."
The result I'll get: "I'll obtain a B.A. in six years."

My rule: _____
_____

My unmet goal: _____
_____

My rule breaker: _____
_____

The result I'll get: _____
_____

Fieldwork:

You can begin to "break" one or more of your societal rules and open doors for yourself by re-viewing them. Ask friends if they have the same rules as you. Does EVERYBODY think you are wrong to take time out from your career? As for the personal rules, are you dealing with a universal law here? Has every writer who has quit a "normal" job starved?

7.04 *Buddy System/Networking*

In the Introduction to this workbook, we introduced you to the concept of a buddy system. Having a buddy is especially critical in this realization phase of your mission work. We hope you let someone in on what you are doing. This is the time to run ideas past your buddy for feedback. Write about your buddy here. Describe how he/she has been helpful and can continue to be supportive in your process of actualizing your mission:

_____

_____

_____

_____

_____

_____

_____

_____

7.05 *Networking*

a) Organize a life mission support group and share your mission statements as well as your interests and activities.
b) Brainstorm ideas for projects with your group.
c) Talk about your intentions at networking functions, events, parties, social occasions—wherever it is appropriate to let people know what you are doing.
d) Give speeches about your mission at professional meetings or speakers' clubs.

7.06 *I Quit! Clearing Out*

Say goodbye to whatever you need to release from your life (your job, for instance?). An actual letter of resignation isn't worth the paper it is written on if you haven't done the emotional and mental releasing beforehand.

Leaving a home, a location, a relationship, or a job is an emotional step which can be difficult to take, especially if you have attachments to friends, places, financial status or routine. You may have sufficient clues that indicate you need to leave—i.e. your body is telling you that enough is enough; you feel the time spent at work is a sacrifice, your job has no more meaning, or you are suffering from the misuse of your skills. In spite of these compelling reasons, if you can't get around to quitting, if you want to wait until the first of the month, or until you qualify for early retirement, or until the kids have left for college or before you visit your second cousin in Alaska, then you still haven't let go.

Write a letter of release and goodbye to whatever person, place, condition or activity that needs to pass from your life. State what served you well throughout your relationship, what you will miss, and why you must let go. End by saying: "I hereby release _____ from my life to make room for my mission." Write that letter here.

Dear_____:

_____

_____

_____

_____

_____

_____

_____

_____

_____

_____

7.07 *Visualizing the Goal Beyond the Goal*

Here's a different way to look at your mission. Imagine that people are in front of a theater waiting to get into a show: YOUR show. They are impatient because the doors have not yet opened, and they are eager to get in. These people are the benefactors of your mission. Imagine them seated in the theater listening to your wisdom. See their faces, hear them clapping, feel their gratitude when they exit the theater; hear what they say about the good you have done for them specifically involving your mission. Write a description of that scene here:

_____

_____

_____

_____

_____

_____

_____

_____

_____

_____

_____

_____

_____

_____

7.08 *Facing Your Fears!*

A mission requires time, commitment, and change. Yes, you will have to make changes before your good gathers momentum. Many people fear what they desire because then, they'll have to spend more time on their mission. Or, they many fear that the commitment required will be too painful. We have already dealt with some of the challenging aspects of your mission search in the section on blocks. When you begin to manifest your mission, you will often encounter potential obstacles.

Here are some common fears expressed by clients:

"I'm afraid I won't be able to sustain my mission over an extended period of time."

"I'm afraid I won't be able to handle what I wanted to manifest."

"I'm afraid I'm not good enough to carry out my mission."

"I'm afraid I'll make the wrong choice and waste my time."

What fears do you have as you embark on manifesting your mission? Describe them here:

_____

_____

_____

_____

_____

_____

_____

_____

_____

_____

_____

7.09 *Commitment: Cheaper by the Dozen*

What you are willing to do for your mission? Be brief.

1. Daily commitment: I agree to spend _____ hours on my mission by doing _____

2. Low PM work: I will work on my low PM of _____ by _____ _____

3. To stay on track, I want help so that I can _____ _____

4. Weekly goals: I agree to spend _____ hours on my mission with the goal of _____ _____

5. I will keep the faith. I will contact _____, my mission buddy. I will call her/him _____ times a week.

6. My monthly mission goals include: _____ _____ and I will know I have completed them when I _____ _____

7. My daily risk, in the service of my mission, will be _____ _____ _____

8. By this time next _____, I plan to be doing
   the following for my mission: _____

   _____

   _____

   _____

9. My spirits are good whenever I _____

   _____

   _____

10. If I intend to do the following to access this good feeling more:

   _____

   _____

   _____

11. If I feel down or feel like I want to stop working on my mission,
    will help myself by_____

   _____

   _____

12. We will reward myself for my mission manifestation work by

   _____

   _____

   _____

7.10 *The Right Stuff: Making your Enjoyments and your Pearls pay off*

For this exercise, you're going to combine one of the "ing" enjoyments you identified in exercise 5.01 with one pearl from your String of Pearls page.

Then, you'll brainstorm ways to generate a project, activity or even livelihood from this combination. (Brainstorming is a technique that has been used in business and in problem solving to generate unlimited ideas without judgment.)

Example: Let's say you wrote "barns" in your notebook and developed the following example: "I enjoy looking at red barns on country highways in Indiana." You have a pearl labeled "visual arts."

List anything and everything that might directly or indirectly relate to "looking at red barns and the visual arts."

Enjoyment: I enjoy looking at red barns on Indiana highways
Pearl: I love the visual arts.

What I could do combining them:

- paint red barns and selling them in galleries
- write a pictorial history of country highways in Indiana
- decorate red barns for motorists to enjoy on country roads

IMPORTANT: You'll get the most out of this exercise if you allow yourself to be imaginative, silly, funny, bizarre, and fanciful. Creativity doesn't thrive on a lot of rules. You are simply generating ideas, so give your imagination free reign. The key here is to list whatever occurs to you as a way to generate income or an activity from your enjoyment/pearl. For now, you do not need to have the skill, talent, resources, time or money to actually do what you brainstorm. Decide later if it's something you are interested in pursuing, and what training or skills you might wish to obtain.

Fieldwork:

Combine your "ing" statement with a different pearl. Let's say your pearl was: enterprise or sports: Your answer might be, for example: "selling red barns to Japanese for use as golf course club houses."

116

Okay, now it's your turn.

Enjoyment:

_____

Pearl:

_____

What I could do combining them: (Generate three examples only from one enjoyment.)

_____

_____

_____

Put your ideas in the Project Section.

7.11 *Diving for Treasures*

Take your mission word, mission statement and your pearls from the String of Pearls Page in Module Six, and transfer them onto separate slips of paper. Put them in a box, shake them up, and take out any three. How can these three pearls could be creatively combined into a career, hobby, avocation, project or other activity?

Let's combine Jacques Cousteau's pearls as an example:

Pearl Combo:
ocean
ecology
film making

Brainstorming Idea:
I could travel to the South Sea and film the effects of pollution on the ocean.

Pearl Combo:
ships
writing
invention

Brainstorming Idea:
I could research and write about inventions of new kinds of ships.

Pearl combo:
physiology
photography
marine life

Brainstorming Idea:
I could photograph divers in the water and study their physical challenges and needs.

For the next week or two, pick three slips daily. Creatively combine them into some concrete endeavor. Return them to the box. Continue to combine three slips to brainstorm new and different combinations. Some combinations may net you ideas quickly; some combinations may take more time. After two weeks you should have a dozen good ideas. Keep a record of them in your project section.

7.12 *The Swiss Cheese Method: Biting off as much as you can chew*

Turn now to your project page. Where do you begin? Prioritize! (see pp. 56 in FYSP). Then, pick one project which particularly attracts you. It must be an activity to which you are willing to devote time on a daily basis.

Example: Let's say your choice is: "I could study the Kodály (or Hungarian) method of teaching music. Is this too big a piece to bite off at one time? Break it down into smaller chunks. You could start by learning Hungarian, taking a music pedagogy course, or reading about Kodály. It may not make you money just yet, but it will get you started on one aspect of your mission.

7.13 *Go! Flow Gently, Sweet Project*

Here's a further way to get started on your project.

Result of Mission: I want to be able to teach the Kodály method of music to 6 year-olds in the United States.

Plan how you want to get from here (where you are at now) to there (result) by developing a flow chart. We call it working backwards from the hole, a technique in golf in which you plan your golf shots starting with the goal (the hole) and working backwards to where you are (the tee). Analogous to this method is to start with your senior year in school and work backwards to where you are now.

To achieve my goal of teaching the Kodály method of music, I must do the following, in reverse order:

Flow Chart:
    Study music in Hungary.
    Leave for Hungary.
    Research travel arrangements.
    Apply to school.
    Save money.
    Get job to pay for part of trip.
    Make a budget.
    Send for forms / scholarships.
    Research grants / scholarships / financial aid.
    Decide where to study.
    Research music schools.
    Learn Hungarian.

119

Now write your project here and design the flow chart needed for the completion of your mission. Remember to work backwards from the hole!

To achieve my goal of _____

_____

_____

_____,

I must do the following, in reverse order: _____

_____

_____

_____

_____

_____

_____

_____

_____

_____

_____

_____

_____

Stay with your project for at least thirty days. Give it all the time and energy you've got. Keep track of your progress, give yourself rewards for what you are doing, tell others about it.

Just because you are about to begin on a project does not guarantee that you will be free of resistance, disappointment, delays, or roadblocks. You may need support as you bravely go down the path.

You can sweeten the project by focusing on the intended results of your project. What will you gain from achieving it? We call that the "goal beyond the goal."

Example: What I desire:
To study the Kodály (or Hungarian) method of teaching music. My goal beyond the goal: To teach this method to 6 year-olds in the USA.

Do that with your project now:

What I desire: _____
_____
_____

My goal beyond the goal: _____
_____
_____

Imagine yourself doing it now!

7.14 *Playing the Field*

Before you plunge into a full-scale campaign, especially if you are applying your mission to a career, test it on a smaller scale. Playing the field may not be the way you like to date, but it sure beats getting into the wrong relationship for an extended period of time. You may know what qualities you want in a person, but you still have to find the one who meets your requirements by playing the field.

Say your mission is to improve the health of women through education. You decide to focus with a project of helping in the field of breast cancer. There are a number of ways to put this plan in motion on a small scale.

a) Volunteer Work

A safe and non-threatening first step is to volunteer at a women's health clinic.

b) Fund Raising

You could get involved with a charitable foundation or participate in a fund raiser for scientific research.

c) Honing Skills

If you have writing skills, you could begin by sending letters to Congress. If your expertise is law, you could find out more about the surgical risks and where women stand from a legal point of view. If it is teaching, you could get more experience in adult education techniques.

d) Informational Interviews

Make a list of those places, organizations or persons which might give you more information on different ways to apply your mission project. Contact people in the field to find out what they are doing. Allow yourself a specific period of time per week for these informational interviews.

e) Going back to school.

For many clients, the mission statement has catapaulted them into returning to school, or getting additional training. Look through catalogs, bulletins, course offerings or visit a local college to see what they have to offer in your field of interest. (See Chapter 5 in FYSP for tips on how to risk.)

f) Researching

Perhaps you don't know what volunteer groups are in your area, or what support groups exist to give you help when you need it. What colleges offer courses that you might need? Make good use of friends, consultants, counselors, libraries, professionals, the Yellow Pages, the Internet or the World Wide Web. This is the Information Age. Information is power, so get it and use it. Remember, fear is often caused by an absence of information.

e) Get More Training or Education

"You never stop learning," a German proverb reminds us. Is there something you need to know before getting started on your project? Life is a learning laboratory. We never outgrow the need to learn. Take classes, go to workshops, seminars, training sessions, study groups, lectures, weekend retreats, and even look for an occasional good program on TV. Pay experts to give you further guidance, and then pass on your wisdom to others. Use the WWW—in short, anything or anyone you can think of to give you information.

7.15 *Keeping myself Afloat*

As you take the plunge, you may encounter a few surprises and disappointments. You may cross a project off your list or head in a direction you hadn't expected. You may change your mind. That's okay, so long as you keep focused on your goal.

a) Ask for Help

To keep afloat, it is important to seek guidance and support from relevant practitioners along the way. Hire someone to do work for you. Do research and ask the librarians for help. Get feedback from peers. If you have access to the Internet, this is an ideal tool for networking your way into a new direction in life. Reach out and get the assistance you need.

b) Organize or Join a Support Group

It is important to sustain contact with those who share your goals and vision. Don't go it entirely alone. While the decisions are yours, the nurturing of others is important to your process. Also, they can be wonderful help to get you unstuck, to keep you encouraged, and to give you ideas when you feel you've run out of them.

c) Speak about Your Mission with Enthusiasm

The more you talk enthusiastically about your path, the more you will gain confidence in your ability to do it. Be aware that some people will try to dissuade and discourage you. Just tell yourself they have their own stuff to deal with. They are coming from their perspective, not yours. The more positively you speak about your mission, the more you will spread goodwill and model enthusiasm to others who are setting out on their own paths.

d) Do What is at Hand

Don't place limits on the mission or the mission process. Know how much time you can comfortably devote to it daily. It all starts with putting one foot in front of the other.

Then do what lies before you. Give your mission project time to emerge and grow. You want to look back and say that you were glad you did the things you loved and that you sang your song. Sometimes, we just have to do what is the next logical thing in order to move forward. Ask yourself what that might be; you'll know.

e) Initiate

If no one is doing what you envision, don't be discouraged. You can be the first to do it! Jump into the breech. Somebody first thought of flying, talking long distance, using a computer, starting a school, beginning a new style of art or music, or designing a geodesic dome.

f) Be Cheerful and Patient

It may take awhile to translate a list of enjoyments and mission pearls into money, or to break rules, to combine slips of paper, or create flow charts. But, you have to start somewhere. Remember that this is a process. Cousteau began to give his passion energy by diving at a young age. How could he know where it would lead? You, too, can do the same. Just follow your heart!

Breaking and Entering

By now, you will see that a project will naturally fall into some form of hobby, work, avocation, activism or volunteer work. If you wish, you can move around in the categories by first starting as a volunteer, then moving into employment, for instance. This is a particularly good starting point for employment, as many jobs evolve out of volunteer work. The important thing is to begin somewhere with your mission, and see where your project takes you.

You can add a second project, depending on your time constraints and energy. A mission will always be expressed in a number of ways. Use the methods we have outlined for ways to identify a new project. Often one project will lead to another quite logically.

In any case, do not rush any project, unless you are desperate for an immediate paying job to cover basic expenses. (In which case you should go to a career counselor or employment agency.)

A second project might translate into a hobby or avocation. So you could be working parallel tracks of hobby and avocation, or volunteer work and employment. But do not overload yourself. One of these projects will naturally emerge as one to which you will devote more time and energy. Or the project might point to a variation on your original idea. Above all, honor the process. For now, give your project or projects a chance to breathe. Remember, all journeys begin with a single step, as the proverb tells us.

You are now ready to take that step. Our blessings.

A few final words:

(Parallel Readings: Chapter 14 and 15 in FYSP)

As we approach and enter the millennium, we are witnessing a time of breathtaking change, both socially and politically. It is hard to keep up with events unfolding on a global scale, let alone our own political and social scene. Governmental and societal systems which worked in the past are falling apart. Others are emerging with renewed vitality. We in North America have learned we have no room to be smug. Our health, education, financial and social service systems are being taxed to the maximum. While we watch our world become ever more international in scope, we are simultaneously challenged with an array of domestic problems such as homelessness, drugs, and urban violence.

Paradoxically, this time of crisis (i.e. as the Chinese define crisis, dangerous opportunity) offers unique opportunities for vision questers. In such a world, options for new enterprises abound. There is a need for services and products which reflect solid values and integrity. Ask yourself how you (and your mission) can contribute.

There is no better time than the present for you to create your dream. Actualized in the smallest form, your mission can be the seed or catalyst for dramatic change, creating a ripple effect far beyond your immediate circle or wildest imagination.

We've given you the encouragement, ideas and necessary tools to be on your way. Now the torch passes into your hands. Remember, this is the most important step you will be taking in your life: you will learn how to recognize and manifest the unique divine talent you are here to express.

Clue Section

Clue Section

(Photocopy as needed)

Clue Section

Projects

(Photocopy as needed)

Project

Title: _____

_____

Justification: How is this project consistent with my
mission? _____

_____

_____

By: Date Entered

To do:

Steps	Contacts: (name/phone)
❑ _____	❑ _____
❑ _____	❑ _____
❑ _____	❑ _____
❑ _____	❑ _____
❑ _____	❑ _____
❑ _____	❑ _____
❑ _____	❑ _____
❑ _____	❑ _____
❑ _____	❑ _____
❑ _____	❑ _____
❑ _____	❑ _____
❑ _____	❑ _____
❑ _____	❑ _____
❑ _____	❑ _____

(Photocopy
as needed)

Project

Title:_____

_____

Justification: How is this project consistent with my
mission?_____

_____

_____

By: Date Entered

To do:

Steps	Contacts: (name/phone)
☐ _____	☐ _____
☐ _____	☐ _____
☐ _____	☐ _____
☐ _____	☐ _____
☐ _____	☐ _____
☐ _____	☐ _____
☐ _____	☐ _____
☐ _____	☐ _____
☐ _____	☐ _____
☐ _____	☐ _____
☐ _____	☐ _____
☐ _____	☐ _____
☐ _____	☐ _____
☐ _____	☐ _____

(Photocopy
as needed)

Notes

Notes

Notes

About the Authors:

Naomi Stephan, Ph.D., is an author, musician, Life Mission coach and educator. She has been involved in Life Mission issues for over 25 years, using her own method to find her mission in life. Naomi has coached thousands of people to find their true purpose in life, a service she now offers exclusively by telephone.

Sue Moore, LCSW, is a licensed psychotherapist who specializes in brief-term and Life Mission coaching. She is an accomplished facilitator of group processes, with more than 25 years experience in community mental health, private psychotherapy and women's issues. Sue is also a poet and playwright.

Naomi and Sue's Life Mission work involves telephone coaching, speaking and training, as well as presenting Finding Your Life Mission™ workshops by invitation across the United States. Clients learn how to identify talents, desires and goals and look beyond the expectations of others to uncover their unique personal mission. Using simple, creative and practical exercises and tools, Naomi and Sue teach how to put this personal mission into immediate action.

For more information on individual coaching, contact Naomi or Sue at 800-957-8888 (message line only) or directly at (704) 298-8003.

Note: *The Fulfill Your Soul's Purpose Workbook* is a guided, home self-study aid which offers information and insight about the subject of Life Mission. It is not intended as psychotherapy, nor is it a substitute for vocational or psychological counseling. The reader is responsible for all insights and actions taken as a result of reading this book.